THE MAKERS
OF HONEY

THE MAKERS
OF HONEY

By Mary Geisler Phillips

Illustrated by Elizabeth Burckmyer

New York

THOMAS Y. CROWELL COMPANY

To the memory of my husband,
Everett Franklin Phillips, and especially to
David, Timothy, Michael, Tappy, and Mary, who
unconsciously helped with the writing of this book.

Contents

Against Idleness and Mischief

How doth the little busy bee
    Improve each shining hour
And gather honey all the day
    From every passing flower!

How skilfully she builds her cell;
    How neat she spreads the wax!
And labours hard to store it well
    With the sweet food she makes.

In works of labour or of skill
    I should be busy too:
For Satan finds some mischief still
    For idle hands to do.

In books, or work, or healthful play,
    Let my first years be passed;
That I may give for every day
    Some good account at last.

—DIVINE AND MORAL SONGS,
    Rev. Isaac Watts (1674-1748)

Note

In this book we shall talk only of the honeybee (the Latin name is *Apis mellifica*). This is the insect that makes the honey we eat. There are other kinds of bees—the bumblebee, carpenter bee, burrowing bee, for example—but when a "bee" is spoken of in this book, it means the honeybee.

1. *Bees of Long Ago*

HOW and when men began keeping bees is anybody's guess. All we know is that cave men left drawings on the walls of a cavern in Spain that show a man taking honeycombs from a crevice in a cliff. We know, too, that the early men of Europe, Asia, and Africa cut down hollow trees in which bees had their homes, and took away the honey. Families ate honey long before they learned to eat bread and milk, and for thousands of years it was the only sweeten-

1

ing known. As far back as 4000 years before Christ one of the Egyptian rulers, King Menes, was known as "The Beekeeper."

Honey was important in those days, as many carvings on tablets of stone and on walls of monuments show. Honeycombs, honey cakes, and sealed jars of honey were placed in tombs as food for the dead. In one ancient tomb the wall shows paintings of a man pouring honey into a pail, and of another kneeling before a pile of hives. All along the wall are drawings of enlarged bees. Honey was one of the most precious offerings made to gods. It is frequently mentioned in the Bible. This is natural, since bees were plentiful in Palestine and honey was used as medicine as well as food.

One of the best-known of Biblical tales is that of Samson, the strong man. One day, on his way to see his sweetheart, a lion attacked him. Samson had nothing to defend himself with, but bravely he grasped the lion and tore it apart with his bare hands. Then he went on, leaving the lion's body where it had fallen. Later he passed that spot again and found that flesh-eating animals had cleaned the bones, and bees had built their comb in the skeleton. He took out some of their honey and carried it home for his family. When it came time for his marriage feast, Samson gave a riddle to be solved by the guests. He said, "Out of the eater came forth meat and out of the strong came forth sweetness." For three days his friends puzzled over what he meant by those words, and then Samson's wife whispered the answer to them. The young men came to Samson and said, "We have the answer! What is sweeter than honey and what is stronger than a lion?"

The early Egyptians learned to do what some beekeepers do today. They followed the blossoming season by floating their colonies on boats along the River Nile. They stopped for a few days at each place where flowers offered nectar and pollen, let the bees gather plentifully, then moved on.

A race of stingless bees, native to Central and South America, has been kept since the time of the Mayas. North America and Australia are the only two countries that have no native bees.

In the days when men fought in armor and citizens protected their cities by building great walled fortresses, bees were used to drive off enemies. When the enemy attacked, hives full of bees would be thrown down upon them from the city walls. The angry, excited bees would rush out to sting anyone within range, seeking

crevices in the knights' armor. They could reach the faces under the visors of helmets, and if you have ever been stung near the eyes, you know how painful it is and how soon your eyes swell shut. What havoc those small defenders could cause!

George DeClyver Curtis, in his book *Bees' Ways,* tells the story of how bees helped the crew of a boat to repulse an enemy. He found the tale in an old magazine called *Western Beekeeper.*

A ship fitting out at Barcelona for a voyage to Cuba and Mexico, in the seventeenth century, was found to have a swarm of bees beneath the upper deck near the bow. The sailors took this for an omen of good luck and did not disturb them. Sure enough, the ship had fair winds and a quick voyage. The chilly weather of the Atlantic at first kept the bees quiet indoors, but when the ship entered warmer waters they began to fly a little every day, never venturing far from the ship's bow.

Nearing Cuba a pirate craft was sighted and the crew manned their guns, but their powder had become damp and they could not fire a shot. The pirates fired several times, one shot striking the ship's bow. Then they laid their vessel across the bow, standing by to board, but little knowing that they were about to attack a floating beehive. The thud of the two hulls meeting, after the jar of the shot, brought out the infuriated bees and the pirates found themselves attacked in turn by an entirely new kind of boarders. Cutlasses were useless against these maddened enemies, the pirates staggered about the deck and fell on their faces, horribly stung.

Their vessel sheered off in haste, while the ship's crew fell on their knees and thanked God for deliverance.

When the ship anchored in the port of Santiago the bees flew at once toward shore and came back with nectar and pollen from the flowers of Cuba. The sailors noticed that some of them fell in the water, so a clever man rigged a canvas platform for an alighting board. The ship sailed on, still with fair winds, and reached the coast of Mexico. There, at Vera Cruz, a priest who had a church near shore came on board and asked the captain to let him take the bees so that the missionaries could have some honey with their coarse fare. But the sailors would not hear of parting with their little mascots—they threatened mutiny. Not to make trouble, the good padre left the ship at once.

But when he had gone, the bees all swarmed out, enveloped the ship in a great cloud and then flew to shore, following the padre's boat. They clustered on a shrub in his dooryard, and when he provided a cask for them they went in at once. The sailors acknowledged that the bees must have been guided all that long way by the will of Providence. They went ashore and marched in solemn procession to the house of the padre, who gave them forgiveness and absolution.

Wherever men have roamed over the face of the earth they have carried bees with them. Spanish, Dutch, and English settlers brought hives of bees with them to North America. Some of their bees left the hives provided for them and made homes for themselves in trees in the forests. When the Indians found them they called them "the white men's flies." Later, when

Australia was settled by the British, bees were imported to that beeless country.

At first the only way to get honey was to find a hollow tree in which bees were living. Some people still like to hunt bee trees. A honey hunter will watch until he happens to see a bee gathering food from a flower. If he sees that it flies toward the woods, he notes the direction. Then he waits for its return for more food from the same flower or from a saucer of sirup he has placed nearby. Again he notes the direction taken by that spark of whirring wings, and follows it. Gradually he may see other homing bees, and so is led to their tree. To get their honey, he must cut the tree down and saw the trunk open. It seems much easier to keep your own bees in man-made hives or to buy your honey in a shop.

Many kinds of hives have been used in different countries. In North Africa and Cyprus, earthenware cylinders are used; in Palestine, domes of dried mud. Hives of straw, dome shaped, called skeps, are still used in many parts of Europe. And if wooden box hives have replaced them, the fronts are often decorated with pic-

tures of landscapes or religious paintings. Sometimes a beeman will carve on the hive the image of a saint.

In the United States bees used to be kept in a section of a hollow log, in part of a barrel, in a box knocked together by the beekeeper, or in skeps. All of these were unsatisfactory because it was hard to get the honey out without injuring many bees.

Then in the 1800's a tremendous change took

place, with the invention of the movable-frame hive, by Lorenzo Lorraine Langstroth, a Congregational preacher and schoolteacher in Philadelphia. In Langstroth's time beemen housed their colonies in boxes that opened at the top. But the bees would glue the lid down tight and would fasten the comb to the sides of the box and add braces of wax from one comb to the next. The glue, a sticky gum called propolis, is gathered by the bees from tree trunks and buds. In cutting away these fastenings and in prying the comb loose, both comb and bees would be harmed.

In the hive that Langstroth invented, a beekeeper could lift the lid, take out a frame of comb and examine the bees on it, and put it back without breaking the comb and without injuring more than a few bees. The Langstroth hive was patented in 1852. It gave a great impetus to beekeeping. By using this hive, one man could care for hundreds of colonies and keep them producing honey and wax year after year. The Langstroth type of hive is now used throughout the world wherever bees are kept on a large scale.

2. Bees, Hives, and Men

BEES are like magicians. They mysteriously change the sweetish water found in flower cups into thick, spicy, sparkling honey. That is something man cannot do. And there's magic in the way they hang motionless for a few hours; and then, from what were empty pockets in their bodies, pull out wax wafers to build honeycomb with. Finally they mold those bits of wax into tiny, fragile, watertight boxes, each six sided, precise, and true in size. Yet the bees have nothing to make measurements with except their feelers and their legs.

People have tried from earliest times to tame the bee as they have tamed the cat, dog, horse, and cow. But a bee never changes its habits to suit man. Not a particle! All that the keepers of bees can do is to try to use what is known of bees' ways to induce bees to produce more and more honey.

A beekeeper may have just a few hives or he may have thousands. An expert alone may manage more than 500 colonies. And each colony— that is, the family in one hive—may contain as many as 70,000 bees. The beeman gives each colony a warm, dry house to live in. He cures his bees of diseases, gives them food for winter, and makes comb-building easy for them. He places the colonies where the bees can reach food and water. Apiary is the name for a collection of beehives. It looks like rows of white boxes.

The modern hive invented by Langstroth is based on his great discovery of the bee space. Langstroth had experimented with all kinds of hives to avoid bees' gluing their combs to the

inside of the hive, but he always had the same trouble when he wanted to look inside one or take honey from it.

Langstroth pondered over this difficulty and watched his bees for long hours at a time, wondering why they persisted in filling up spaces he wanted left open. Then he noticed that the bees did not build comb or stuff glue in spaces that were just wide enough and high enough for the passage of one bee. This bee space is from $\frac{3}{16}$ to $\frac{5}{16}$ inch in size.

The idea came to him as he was driving home in his horse-drawn buggy from his apiary which stood on ground that is now part of the campus of the University of Pennsylvania. He could hardly wait to have his helper, a cabinetmaker, build him a hive in which every layer of comb would be surrounded on all sides by an open bee space, and the same distance would separate the cover from the body of the hive. No smaller spaces, no larger ones allowed!

Just as he thought, the bees stopped filling the smaller spaces with glue, and stopped building comb between the combs hanging parallel in the frames.

A standard hive is a wooden box with both top and bottom removable. It is large enough to hold 10 oblong wooden frames, each measuring $9\frac{1}{8}$ inches by $17\frac{5}{8}$ inches. These frames will be filled with honeycomb. The beekeeper looks into his hive and examines the bees by taking off the cover and lifting out a frame at a time, with bees clinging to both its sides.

The frames hang side by side, parallel to the long sides of the box. The walls of the hive fit snugly on the bottom board, but at the front an open space ⅜ inch high is left across the width of the hive. This is the entrance. The bottom board can be reversed to make the height of the entrance ⅜ inch for cold weather. It also extends out beyond the rest of the hive, making a porch. This is called the alighting board. The whole hive can be lifted off the bottom board to clear it of trash and dead bees, or the dead bodies of enemies. The hive is often raised a little from the grass to keep the bottom board from rotting and to let air pass under it.

The box containing frames, without the bottom board and lid, is the hive body, in which the young bees are raised. Then the beekeeper, who hopes to take honey from his bees, inserts between the hive body and the cover a super. This is a shallower box of frames (or it may be the same height as the body) in which the bees will store their honey. The queen is kept from laying eggs in this part of the hive by means of a queen excluder, a metal plate or grill with spaces large enough to let a worker pass through but not large enough for the queen. Therefore she cannot get into the super and lay eggs there. Bees like to store nectar in the upper part of the hive, so it is natural for them to go into a super and, finding empty comb there, fill the cells for the beekeeper.

A hive, then, is made up of a bottom board, hive body, queen excluder, super, an inner cover, and a heavy wooden lid.

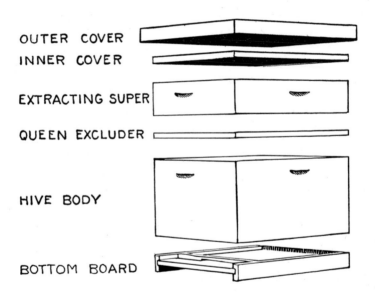

OUTER COVER

INNER COVER

EXTRACTING SUPER

QUEEN EXCLUDER

HIVE BODY

BOTTOM BOARD

In the United States more than 500,000 bee-keepers own more than 5 million colonies of bees. With from 60,000 to 70,000 bees in each colony, you can see how many bees that makes. Some beekeepers own just one or two hives, but men who make their living selling honey, wax, and sometimes bees themselves may own several thousand colonies. The amount of honey produced in the United States each year is about 220 million pounds.

Bees have one characteristic that many insects do not have—they hoard food. Instead of flying to a warm climate for the winter as some birds do, or sleeping through the cold months as bears do, bees remain active inside the hive. They huddle together and keep themselves warm by beating their wings as we might stamp our feet to warm them. Of course bees need food for such activity, and that is why they try to gather enough food during the summer to last them over winter. Even in the tropics, where flowers bloom throughout the year, the bees continue to store up food; and in cooler climates they will gather supplies as long as they have a place to store them. It is this characteristic that the bee-keeper takes advantage of. As soon as the storage cells are filled in one super, he takes it away and gives the bees another to fill. And the bees oblige by working themselves to death for him.

Bees breathe the same air that we do, drink water, eat food, live in families, and were doing all these things long before there were any people on the earth. How many centuries they were living before man appeared we do not know. Indeed, many things about bee life remain a mystery, even though these insects have been studied for thousands of years.

These small creatures cannot reason, but in some unknown way they have learned that to survive they need to live together cooperatively in a large group. Everything they do is for the good of all. A single bee will starve before letting the queen of the colony go hungry. To protect the colony from enemies, a worker will use her sting even though that is certain death for her. Among honeybees we see plainly the urge most living creatures have to help the race continue, no matter what may happen to a single member.

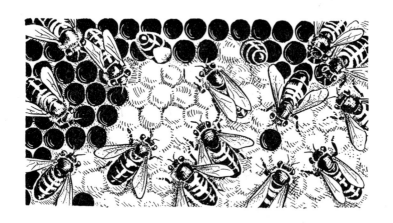

3. Family Life in the Hive

YOUR family, as well as most of the other families you know, is made up of your father, mother, brothers, and sisters. If there is a baby in the family, your mother has to give hours each day to caring for it. A baby must be cuddled, bathed, fed often with special food, and taken outdoors for air and sunshine.

Parents give their children a great deal of attention until they are grown up. Even when you become old enough to be away from home each day at school, your father and mother feed and clothe you, love you, amuse you, and help you to become a good adult. Only after schooling is over is one likely to leave home to take a job and begin a family of one's own.

The family of the honeybee is nothing like that. Far from it! To begin with, each family, or colony, may be made up of as many individuals as there are in a good-sized city. They have little to do with the families in the other hives nearby. If a bee from another hive comes to the door, she is turned away, unless perhaps she carries a load of food that the colony can use.

It is each family for itself among bees. Usually a colony contains only one mother, called the queen, who seldom goes out after she begins the job of egg-laying. She pays little attention to her children. All she does is lay eggs. The father, called a drone, dies before his children are born. So who takes care of the children? That is the business of the grown-up sisters, the workers. Not only do they feed and care for the helpless young ones; they clean the house, guard the entrance, ventilate the hive, gather food, and even

feed their brothers, also called drones. During the summer the colony consists of the queen, thousands of workers, and only some hundreds of drones.

The most amazing thing about this family is the way they all get along together. No sister refuses to do her job; she knows without being told what her work is to be for the day and goes to it, while the brothers do nothing to help. The big, bumbling, awkward drones sit on the comb, doing no work but begging for food. And any passing sister stops to feed them.

Can you imagine such a household of human beings? Can't you see the turmoil it would be in most of the time? There would be the lazy one who shirks, the vain one who won't scrub because she has nice hands, and the complainer who thinks nothing the others do is right, and— well, it makes your brain reel just to think of the confusion. When people work together, they need a manager to plan the work and to see that each person carries out his part. That is what is done in large business organizations and in factories.

But a colony of bees runs the machinery of daily living with no signs of a boss, no signs of friction. How bees have been able to work out such a way of life is one of the wonders of nature that has not yet been solved. This is communism carried out to its logical conclusion: a society in which no one does anything to please himself, nor works for any profit to himself. The individual gets room and board in return for laboring from the beginning of life to death without stopping. Each bee follows the fixed round of living without question. And everything is done only for the good of the colony.

4. *The Worker Bee's Body*

BEFORE we talk more of the life that goes on inside the hive, let us look closely at a single worker bee. When you see one flying, you get only a vague idea of a yellow and brown crystal-winged insect that darts like a point of light through the air. She always seems to be in a hurry. If you take a dead bee in your hand and examine it, you find that it has a fat, fuzzy body, two pairs of fragile wings, and six legs.

If you look at a bee under a magnifying glass,

you will see that her body structure is entirely different from ours. Rub off the fuzz and you find a hard bony covering which completely encases the soft organs. The bee can bend only at overlapping joints, where the inner part of the overlap is thinner and softer than the rest. A bee needs the protection of this hard skin, for she has many enemies.

In speaking of our own bodies, we talk of the head, thorax or chest, abdomen, arms, and legs. The bee's body too may be divided into parts: head, thorax (to which the legs and wings are attached), and a jointed abdomen.

The head contains the brain, and on the outside are the eyes, the antennae, and the many parts of the bee's mouth. The inside of the thorax is filled mostly with big muscles that move the wings and legs. The abdomen holds the organs that digest food, the sex organs, large air sacs, and the sting. The bee has no lungs and no heart like ours. She breathes with every part of her body through small tubes that take air into her air sacs. In place of a heart she has a tube that runs the length of the abdomen, with valves opening on either side to take in and let out blood.

The bee is better equipped than we are to get around in the world, for she can move by land or by air under her own power, and can go long distances for her size. Even for short distances we are likely to go on wheels. And if we use a wheeled vehicle, it is a *manufactured* bicycle, auto, trolley, train, bus, or wagon. For air travel we use a complicated airplane, and a boat for water travel. The bee, who travels mostly by air, needs no machine nor any outside fuel for flying. She has everything she needs—four wings and heavy muscles to make them go, as well as her six legs. The back wings are small and they have a row of hooks which can be fastened to the edge of the larger front wings. Together the four wings make a broad flying surface.

All that a bee has to do is to spread her wings, hook them together, give a push with her feet and up she goes. She can outmaneuver the fanciest stunts of an airplane. She can hover indefinitely over a hive, with her head always turned toward it to fix its location; she can dart in a

HEAD   THORAX   ABDOMEN

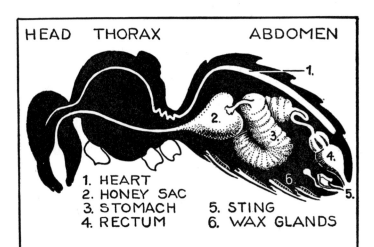

1. HEART
2. HONEY SAC
3. STOMACH   5. STING
4. RECTUM   6. WAX GLANDS

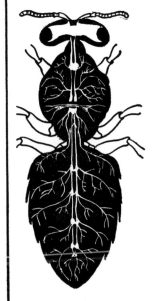

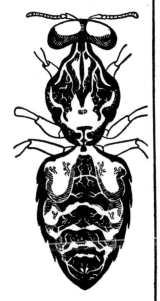

NERVOUS
SYSTEM

AIR SACS WHICH
SUPPLY OXYGEN

straight line upward or forward, fly backward, and at full speed drop to the alighting board and stop short without skidding.

The six legs of the bee have a great advantage over our arms and legs, for not only do they have an extra joint between knee and ankle, but they are all equipped with tools. No wasting of time looking for hammer, brush, comb, pickax, spoon, shovel or trowel. They are all part of the legs of the bee.

On the extra joint of the first pair of legs is a delicately made cleaner for the antennae, which are always tapping ahead like a blind man's cane. The cleaner has a hinged, curved top piece which opens so that an antenna can slip into a hollow groove. Then the top shuts down, pressing the antenna against a fringe of bristles. The bee draws the antenna through the bristles, and every bit of dirt is brushed off.

On the next pair of legs is a most useful tool, a curved, pointed tusk. Its greatest use is to pry loose the sticky pollen packed in a basket on the last pair of legs.

The hindmost pair of legs is the most ingenious. Where the knee bends are two sharp-toothed edges that form a pair of shears or pincers. The bee uses this tool to grasp and pull out flat wafers of wax from pockets on the abdomen. The joint below the knee is broadened and hollowed out on the side away from the body, and the edge of the hollow is fringed with hairs. This makes a basket into which, while flying, the bee packs the pollen she brushes from her hairy body, shoving it down tight to make a ball of dough that does not fall out. The ball may be

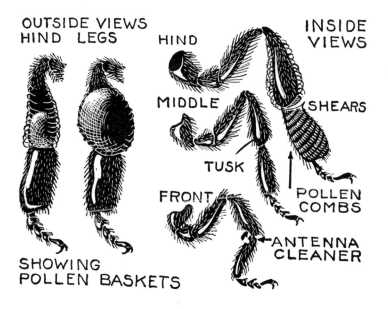

OUTSIDE VIEWS
HIND LEGS

HIND

INSIDE VIEWS

MIDDLE

SHEARS

TUSK

FRONT

POLLEN COMBS

ANTENNA CLEANER

SHOWING
POLLEN BASKETS

almost as big as the bee's head, a heavy load when both pollen baskets are full.

John Burroughs described the way a bee loosens her load on each hind leg when she is home and ready to put it into a cell. He says she "kicks it off as one might his overalls or rubber boots, making one foot help the other." But it is a little harder than that. The spur or tusk on the middle leg must pry the tightly packed pollen out, the spur on one leg unloading the ball in the basket on the opposite leg. The pollen is stored for food.

The bee's mouth is not a bit like ours. It has strong, jagged jaws that work sidewise, not up and down as do ours. Those jaws can crush, bite, and grind. Below them is a shiny, brown, sharp instrument which hangs from the mouth like an

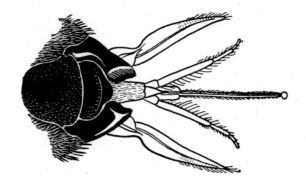

elephant's trunk. Under the microscope you can see that this trunk, or proboscis, is the pulled-out lower lip, made up of several strips that fit together to form a tube. Inside the tube is the tongue, long and slender, with a spoon-shaped tip bristling with hairs.

How does the bee eat with such a mouth? Well, if there is just a tiny bit of nectar to be taken from a flower, she sucks it up with the tip of her tongue. If there is much liquid to be taken, she sucks it through the tube as you suck soda through a straw. When the bee is not using her trunk, it lies flat against the under side of the thorax.

The two jointed feelers, or antennae, that you can easily see stretching out from the head of the bee are touch organs. Watch the bee closely and you will see those antennae almost always moving this way and that, touching here and there. How much the bee learns about her surroundings from her antennae has not yet been discovered, but along these feelers have been found many tiny pits, plates, and pegs—mysterious organs that may or may not help the bee to hear, smell, and exchange information with her mates. The antennae may also be measuring tools that help to make the cells of honeycomb always the right size.

On each side of the bee's head is a large bulge. This is the compound eye, made up of many small eyes pressed close together. In the center

of what we might call the forehead are three pinpoint eyes, the simple eyes.

How much a bee can see with her hundreds of small eyes and with her three simple eyes is not known, for they are all very different from ours. Beemen have discovered that the bee can tell dark from light, can distinguish polarized light that we cannot recognize, can tell differences in color, and can see moving objects. It is probable that the big compound eyes are for distant vision, and the three simple ones for distinguishing the quality of light.

A famous scientist, Dr. Karl von Frisch, who has studied bees' ways for a lifetime, found through experiments that bees can tell one color from another. On a table near his apiary he placed squares of differently colored cardboard, blue, red, yellow, gray, black, and white. On each square he put a saucer, all empty except the one on the blue card. In the blue-card saucer he placed a little sugar sirup. Then he sat nearby to watch what might happen.

After a while, a hovering bee found the sirup. She put her forefeet on the edge of the dish, dipped her long tongue down in, and sipped the sugar. While she was enjoying herself, Dr. von Frisch touched her back with a bit of white paint, so that he would know her if she ever came back. The bee flew away.

It was not long before she returned with several other bees and they all darted to the saucer on the blue card, dipped their tongues in and sipped, wagging the back part of their bodies as if to show how much they enjoyed the sweet. The scientist touched the back of each with a bit of paint of a different color from that used on the first scout.

When they had filled their stomachs and flown away, Dr. von Frisch moved around the position of the food and the blue card among the other cards, and each time the bees went to the blue card. Then he removed the food altogether from the blue card and the bees still came back to that card. Soon the marked bees were back with a few more of their friends. They hovered over the table, then darted to the empty saucer on the blue card. In vain they tried to find something to eat in that saucer because that was where the sirup had been before! Dr. von Frisch realized that they recognized the color blue.

After the bees had left the blue card, Dr. von Frisch placed the sirup on a gray card, and one bee was more persistent than the rest. She kept on trying to find the sirup and at last hit upon the right saucer. When she had her fill, she flew away. Dr. von Frisch had marked her, and

watched to see whether she would come back with companions. Sure enough, she soon returned and a row of bees formed around the edge of the saucer on the gray card, each one avidly sipping the sweet. These too received a dab of paint, so that the watcher could tell again whether the same bees would return.

Back they came, with some of their comrades, and again ate their fill. When they had made four or five trips, always darting right to the saucer on the gray, Dr. von Frisch again used a different color card with the food saucer containing the sirup.

This time, when the painted bees came back for more, they were confused. They flew to the saucer on the gray card, but it was empty. They hovered over the table, undecided what to do, and finally left without discovering that the filled saucer was on the table. But this time it was resting on a card of still a different color. After many such experiments Dr. von Frisch became convinced that bees recognize many different colors: they are blind to red, but they distinguish other colors from gray and may be trained to distinguish blue-green from blue and from yellow. Ultraviolet, which is a color our eyes cannot see, is a distinct color for the bees. So the range of colors for bees seems to be yellow, blue-green, blue, and ultraviolet. They often visit white flowers and other plants with most inconspicuous flowers, but to them these may appear colored, because often such blossoms absorb or reflect ultraviolet rays.

Behind the head is the thorax, to which the head is attached by a thin thread of neck. The wings spring from the upper side of the thorax, the six legs from the under side. Inside the skeleton of the thorax are heavy muscles that move the legs and wings.

Now comes a slender, short waist. Behind it is the largest portion of the body, the abdomen, where the stomach is located. The abdomen is fuzzy with hairs which wear off as the bee grows older. Under the hairs the abdomen is made up of overlapping bands. If the bee sucks up much nectar, the stomach is filled. Then the overlapping lessens and the body swells out like an accordion.

At the end of the abdomen is the sting, the part of the bee you hear most about. That sting, kept inside the body until it is needed, is like a two-edged narrow knife split down the middle. The outer edge of each blade is not smooth but is

toothed along its length like the edge of a saw. Besides this sharp instrument there are two soft flaps that let the bee know when the sting is against the object to be punctured. Then the sharp pointed sword is thrust in and poison is pumped into the wound.

The sting does not go in with a single thrust. First one side of the knife jabs in, then the other edge drives in a little deeper, then the first edge in turn. No wonder it hurts! Because the saw edges turn backward, the bee cannot pull her sting out of the wound. She tries to—she struggles, but it will not come loose. With a last desperate effort in trying to pull away, the bee tears her own body to pieces. Left behind with the sting are muscles and other parts from inside the abdomen as the poor bee drops dead. She always sacrifices her life when she attempts to protect the hive through stinging an enemy, but she may not die immediately. If you are ever stung, be sure to scrape out the sting with your fingernail immediately; otherwise it keeps on pumping in poison.

The bee we have been talking about is a worker, the kind you see flying from the hive on a summer morning, or hovering over a field of clover, or sitting on a flower, dipping her long tongue to the bottom of the blossom. The other members of the family, the drones and the queen, fly out only occasionally so that you usually do not see them unless you take off the lid of the hive and lift out a frame. We shall speak of these bees later.

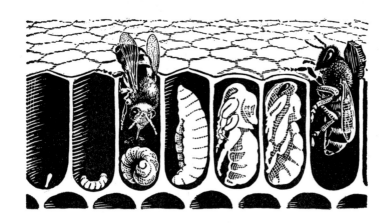

5. *The Worker Bee from Egg to Young Adult*

HOW HAPPY a poultryman would be if his hens would lay in one day as many eggs as the queen bee does! He'd be still happier if he didn't have to feed his hens and keep them clean. But he has no such helpers as the queen bee has and must do the work himself.

The bee egg is about ¹⁄₁₆ inch long. It looks like a slightly curved hot dog, with the head end a little larger than the rest of the body. Its cradle is a hexagonal cell of wax. About three days after the egg is laid, the baby bee breaks out. Now it is a larva, not a bit like the bee you see flying on a summer day. It is a white, soft, curved grub, with no legs, wings, or eyes, but it has a huge mouth which is usually open for food. The mouth leads into the stomach, which takes up most of the space inside the body.

The baby bee grows at a terrific rate. It increases in size so fast that, if you had grown at the same rate just after you were born, you would have been as large as an elephant when you were four days old!

Such rapid growth requires a lot of food and the nurse bees are kept busy feeding hundreds of young ones. One scientist counted nearly ten thousand feedings for one larva. Just as a mother changes her baby's formula as the child grows older, so the bee nurse changes the larva's meals to suit its age. The larva bursts out of its skin about once a day until the nurse stops feeding it.

For the first three days the larvae are fed "royal jelly," a milky white substance produced by glands in the nurse bee's head. This is given with water, but whether the two are mixed or are fed separately we do not know. The older larvae receive honey and pollen for their meals.

On about the sixth day, the nurses know that it is time for a larva to rest, so they stop the feeding and put a lid of wax over the top of the cell in which the larva lies. Inside this sealed box the larva then prepares itself for a change in its life. It spins a delicate silken cover and winds it over itself, head and all. This is the cocoon. The creature inside is called a pupa. Workers, drones, and queens all go through the larval and pupal periods. The organs of the adult bee are developing while it is in a cocoon, and in twelve days (for a worker bee) the body of the pupa has developed the intricate organs needed by the adult.

At the end of the pupation, the young adult, who now has jaws to bite with, cuts a slit in the lid of the cell and, sometimes helped by a worker, pulls itself out to the surface of the comb. It finds itself in a bustling world of older bees.

Now let us follow a brand new worker bee. For a day or two, she just sits there watching, as

if to get her bearings. With moving bees all
around her, each one intent on her own business,
paying no attention to the young one, it would
not be surprising if the new bee were somewhat
confused. But soon, as if to start the life of a
grown-up properly, she begins to rub herself
down. Head and eyes are brushed over first, then
antennae and legs, and finally her downy body.
She uses her legs skillfully and intently, stopping
now and then to put out her tongue to receive a

snack from the tongue of an older bee passing by. Gradually she seems to wake up to the idea that she is a member of a large family and had better do her share of the housekeeping.

Her first jobs are inside the hive, and that is as it should be because her eyes are still covered with hairs and she probably would not be able to see her way about outdoors. The hairs fall off later. Inside the dim hive her antennae guide her. About the third day, she begins to stick her head into empty cells. She may remain in one for several minutes; and, if it is not ready for the queen, she cleans and polishes it. Old combs become thick and dark and take on a high polish because of the many old cocoons left behind by bees reared in those cells. Queens seem to prefer to lay eggs in old comb, where other bees have been raised.

For some time the young bee works at her first job with zeal. But then she may take several hours' rest, sitting idly on the comb. No one says, "For heaven's sake, get to work!" No one says, "If you're not going to work yourself, get out of my way!" Each bee tends to her own business, letting the rest go their own ways. That seems to work very well in the bee colony.

How any bee finds out what, when, and how to do her tasks no one knows, but every young worker bee starts to do the housekeeping chores as if she had always been doing them. A child has to be taught his tasks and at first does them fumblingly, often forgetting what comes next, but a bee does her work perfectly the minute she is out of her cradle.

6. *Nurses, Comb-Builders, Policemen*

AFTER a day or two of being a cleaning woman, the young bee changes her work to that of baby-nurse. She now goes to the cupboards holding honey and sucks up a stomachful, or she may go to the part of the comb where pollen is stored and pry loose some of it with her jaws. Pollen is sometimes mixed with honey before storage, or it may be mixed with honey in the nurse's mouth before being placed in the cell for a larva. These two foods make up the meals for older larvae. A nurse puts some of the honey and pollen from her honey stomach into a cell and the larva inside moves around until it comes in contact with the food. The nurse goes on and feeds another older larva, leaving the feeding of the smallest ones to more experienced nurses. A scientist counted that each cell was visited an average of more than 2000 times for cell cleaning, larval inspection, larval feeding, and cell capping. All such visits together consumed 10 hours and 16 minutes of time per larva.

Larvae just hatched need, as we have seen, royal jelly, which is rich in food value. How the nurses are able to tell the difference in age among the hundreds of larvae is not known, but each age receives the mixture of food needed for growth at that stage. The glands which produce royal jelly develop when the nurses are about five or six days old, and then it becomes their task to feed the just-hatched larvae, giving them not only the jelly but water carried into the hive by field bees.

This work they continue to do until they are

about 13 days old, when their royal jelly glands dry up.

Next, the wax glands develop and the young adults are ready for the job of building honeycomb when they are from 12 to 18 days old. One bee cannot build comb by herself. She needs the help of dozens of bees of her age. They are all skilled without having had to learn this trade.

First the builders fill themselves with honey, for this is work requiring a great deal of energy. Then a row of them fastens a ridge of wax against the underside of the top bar of a frame, and there they cling by their forelegs. Now others hook their legs into the legs of the bees on the top bar near them until a long string is formed. When the bees at the ends of these living strings reach the bottom of the frame, they move toward each other until they connect, thus making a loop. Soon many loops, one inside another, connect to form a hanging sheet of bees.

The hanging bees now rest motionless, waiting for wax to ooze from glands into eight small pockets on the underside of the abdomen. In about 24 hours the wax that has poured into the

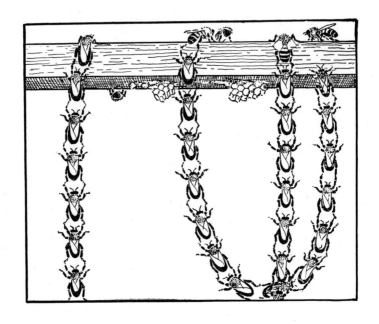

pockets has hardened into frail, almost transparent wafers, somewhat like tiny potato chips. The wafers are colorless but on exposure may become tinged with yellow or red.

When the wax is ready, the hanging bees disperse and carry their building material to the place where new comb is to be built out from the first ridge of wax. A bee will pull a wafer from a pocket with a back leg, pass it forward to the forelegs, and grasp it with the jaws. There it is chewed and mixed with saliva, and then one bee alone or two bees working in partnership pat and pull it into position.

All work harmoniously and do not seem to get in one another's way, as bit by bit is added to form the six-sided cells. Although the bees have only their antennae and legs for plumb line and rule, the results of their labor are cells generally true and nearly uniform in size and shape.

In order to help the bees produce honey faster and build uniform comb, beekeepers first insert a stiff layer of wax, called a foundation, in each frame, as a picture is placed in a picture frame. This foundation has a six-sided impression on each side outlining the shape of the cells, and on this the bees build up the comb on both sides.

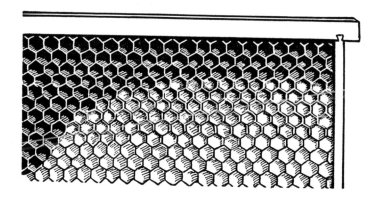

The cells are slanted upward a little by the bees so that the watery nectar will not spill out.

Beekeepers used to glue a bit of old comb into the top of a frame so that the comb builders would not have to start from scratch. But now foundation serves this purpose better.

To prevent the foundation from sagging in the frame in hot weather, beekeepers make each sheet stronger by pressing two fine wires into the wax horizontally a few inches apart. The bees disregard the wires that hold the comb firm. With straight, even bottoms all prepared for the building out of the sides of the cells, straight combs are assured.

One of the last of the indoor jobs for young workers is the difficult and dangerous one of guarding the entrance at the bottom of the front of the hive, with the alighting board in front of it.

A scientist watched sentries day after day in a glass hive. He saw that when the first fliers start out in the early morning, and again toward evening, the guards are especially watchful. They guard the doorway carefully also during cool weather, when not much food is available and

robbers may try to steal their supply. Guards will rush at a bee about to enter and, with half-opened wings, touch her all over with their antennae. If they find from her odor that she is a member of the family, she is allowed to pass; but just let a robber bee from another colony try to get by! Then, not just one but a dozen policemen hasten to attack the unwelcome guest, sting her to death, and throw her body out. Like human beings, some bees seem to relish the job of being a guard much more than do others; and how long a bee remains on the police force seems to depend on her enthusiasm for the work.

Other jobs that need doing inside the hive before a worker becomes a field bee will be taken up in the next chapter.

7. *Odd Jobs for Young Workers*

DURING the latter part of the nursing period, young bees are often seen wandering through the hive, stopping now and then to rest, or running away if an old bee gives them a shove. But when they become somewhat accustomed to being pushed, they do a little shoving themselves and go where they please. During their explorations, they may come near the doorway through which daylight appears. The coming and going of older bees seems to give them courage, and one will suddenly venture forth to try her wings. Instead of being in the warm, dark hive, she finds herself in sunshine surrounded by delicious odors, green grass, and blue sky. We can only guess, but it must be wonderful fun—something like one's first ride in a plane.

The newly flying bee is cautious. She does not venture far from the hive and always keeps her head turned toward it, flying in small, then larger and larger circles. A scientist who watched marked bees on their early flights saw that they took directions as they flew so that they could always find their way back.

After a first short flight, back goes the refreshed worker to her job. Her work now becomes varied. She may help young bees to break their way out from their cells; she may carry rubbish out of the hive or pack pollen down tightly in the cells where other bees have put it; or she may take food from the mouths of field bees and store it in the proper cells.

Another part of her work is to be a fanner. From the entrance to the top of the hive the fanners take turns standing in rows and beating their wings to drive fresh air into the hive and over the cells containing freshly gathered nectar. In this way moisture is driven from the nectar so that it becomes the thick sticky honey that

we know. These fanners are air-conditioners too who keep the hive ventilated and at the right temperature.

One more job for young bees is occasionally to act as honey jars. When the flow of nectar is

unusually heavy, the field bees bring in more
than enough to fill all the cells available. But
they do not stop on that account. Instead they
pour out the nectar into the mouths of young
bees who hold it in their honey stomachs until
more comb is given them by the beekeeper or

until they can build more. Such living honey pots
can be seen in the hive, their abdomens swollen
with all the nectar they contain.

Young bees also serve as errand girls, taking
nectar from the tongues of the busy field bees
as they come home with a load in their honey
stomachs. The young bees suck it into their

stomachs, then carry it to the cells set aside for the fresh nectar. It is thought that some chemical change may take place in the nectar while it is in the young bee's stomach and mixing with juices there. They do not fill one cell before going to another. Instead they spread out the sweet liquid, smearing it against the bottoms and walls of many cells. This gives a larger surface for the evaporation of water from the nectar. Smart girls! How do these bees know that? This is another mystery of the hive.

When field bees hurry to cells and kick off the wads of pollen they carry, it is the job of inside workers to pound it down and press it into a solid mass by butting it with their heads, or pushing with their jaws. So it seems that indoor bees do any odd jobs that come to hand and fill in wherever they are most needed. No one directs them as they go about their various duties, but they seem ready and willing to help with any and all chores, handy and skillful, forever busy.

8. Drones—
the Playboys of the Hive

ON ANY MILD, sunshiny day in summer, when worker bees are rushing to and fro at the hive, carrying in heavy loads of food and water, you may see other bees in the air around the bee yard. These fly aimlessly and rather clumsily, buzzing loudly as if they enjoyed having nothing to do but exercise their wings. They are the drones, the brother bees, who never help with any of the household chores. In fact, they can't work, for their tongues are not fitted for gathering stores; they have no sting with which to help protect the family; they have no wax glands needed in building comb, and they carry no tools on their legs. Their loud buzz sounds threatening, but it means nothing except perhaps, like some small boys, they can't help being noisy.

Drones move awkwardly, for their bodies are bigger and thicker than those of either the queen or the worker. Their abdomens are short and stubby, without the graceful taper of that of the queen; their heads are larger also, and their two bumps of eyes meet in the middle of the top of the head. The workers seem to like to have drones around during the summer and willingly feed the big loafers, who have tremendous appetites.

Drone eggs are laid in special drone cells, which are slightly larger than those intended for worker eggs. The egg hatches in three days and the larva that emerges is fed for about a week. By that time the fat white grub almost fills the cell. The workers shut the grub in with a lid of

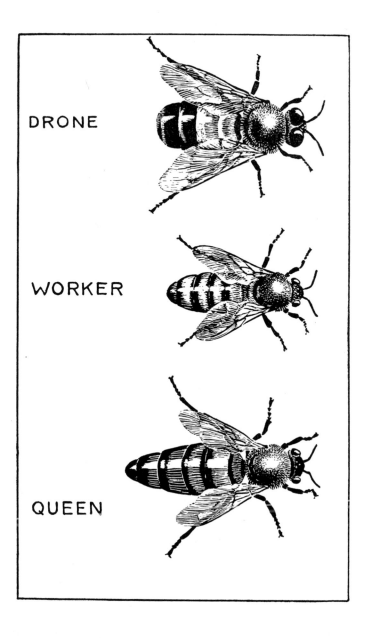

DRONE

WORKER

QUEEN

wax, dome shaped to give room for the head. If you look at a sheet of comb, you can readily tell which cells hold drones because of the cobblestone appearance of that part of the comb. Where the wax surface is smoother, worker pupae are enclosed.

It takes from 24 to 25 days for a drone egg to become an adult, three days longer than for a worker bee to develop. When the fully formed drone cuts his way out of his cell, he begins what to us looks like a life of fun and idleness. He roams about the hive or sits where workers have to stumble over him, begging for food and getting it from the tongues of his sisters. He seems sometimes to realize that he may be in their way, for often he does his loafing on the outer edges of the frames away from the heaviest traffic and away from the rows of fanners.

Before flying out in the late morning, after the dew is off the grass, a drone will touch a worker with outstretched tongue, and she will stop to transfer food from her tongue to his. After eating, he goes outside and stands on the alighting board leisurely brushing out his antennae, looking for all the world, as one author says, like "a gentleman stroking his moustache." Then he flies about until hungry again, when he returns for another handout.

Only when the air is cold and windy, and the sky is cloudy, does the drone stay indoors. At other times, as soon as the sun is well up he is off, flying hither and yon, but not going far from home. His clusters of tiny eyes give him exceedingly keen eyesight, his wing muscles are strong, and he has a fine sense of smell. So equipped, he is ready for his lifework of mating with a queen. Although he seems to be flying just for fun, he is always alert and ready to overtake a young queen. She is sure to take to the air some fine day for her mating, and he must be able to recognize her and fly after her.

It is thought probable that the queen trails a special scent recognizable by drones as she darts from the hive and zooms up into the blue. Off she goes and the hundreds of drones that have been hanging around the apiary dash after her. She is a swift and strong flier, yet because she wants to be caught, she will probably turn about

and fly back toward the oncoming rush of drones.

The strongest and swiftest male catches her and clasps her to him, face to face. A sharp pop or explosion occurs as he pushes all his complicated male organs out from his body, and places one organ, a slender tube, into a waiting sac in the queen's body. As they fly, a substance from his tube enters her sac. This is the sperm which is able to fertilize the eggs already growing in her body. Every fertilized egg will develop into female bees (queens and workers); unfertilized eggs become drones.

When the drone's mission is accomplished, the queen tries to pull away but the male organs are tightly embedded. Struggling to separate, the drone and queen tumble to the ground near the queen's hive. He may be from that hive too, or he may be from another, but the queen has steered herself toward home. The drone is dying, for a good portion of his insides are pulled away, and when the queen is at last able to free herself, those organs dangle from the end of her abdomen.

The drone has placed inside the queen enough sperm to fertilize eggs for several years; and, once more back home, she begins her life-long job of laying eggs.

The drone who mated is dead, but there are hundreds of other drones who still have a chance of mating, since a queen will probably be coming out from every hive in the apiary. Each hive usually contains only one queen but several hundred drones.

It is an expensive business for the colony to support so many drones when only one is needed to fertilize their queen, but the workers seem not to mind feeding the idlers so long as food is plentiful. They treat them as pets. But when fall approaches, and fewer flowers are offering nectar and pollen, and the sun is less warm, with more rainy days, then the colony seems to realize that they cannot afford to be so extravagant. One of the first tasks in preparation for winter is to get rid of so many mouths to feed.

Some drones have died during the summer, some have been eaten by birds, but many remain. In the fall the workers refuse to put food into the pleading outstretched tongues of drones. If one tries to make his way to the storeroom to help himself, he is treated roughly and hustled to the bottom board of the hive. There the outcasts must stay, growing gradually weaker for want of food. Finally they die of starvation, or are shoved outside to die when too weak to put up a fight. Their bodies are carried off a little way and dropped in the grass, or pushed over the edge of the alighting board.

From our point of view this looks like a sad ending to a happy life. But since drones cannot think any more than workers can, we have no way of knowing whether they have any viewpoint at all on the matter. They are like machines that act in a certain way when a certain key is pressed. Drones fly whenever the warm sun shines—is the sun the key that draws them outside? They chase a queen when they catch her scent—is odor the key that makes them follow her? The drone's body touches the queen's—is that touch the key that causes them to mate? We have no answers to these questions—all we know is that the drone has performed his duty to the colony and has fulfilled his destiny. Now he is dead.

9. The Queen—
Mother of the Colony

WHEN you think of a queen, you probably think of beautiful robes and jewels, and much pomp and circumstance. You have also probably heard how hard a queen must work at governing her subjects, and how she is surrounded by many people during most of her waking hours.

The queen in a bee colony also leads a life of hard work, and she also has a circle around her, following every move she makes. But, unlike a human queen, a bee queen has nothing to do with governing the colony and, in fact, is more stupid than the workers. She has to be fed and groomed. Most of her life is spent inside the hive where she does nothing but lay eggs day and night, with only short periods of rest and time out for eating. Just a few times in her life does she have an opportunity to use her wings and see green trees and blue sky and feel sunshine on her back.

A new queen may be chosen because the present queen is old and the bees may feel the need for a new queen. Or maybe they are so crowded in the hive that they feel the urge to leave and start a new home. They will need to take a queen with them, but they cannot leave the colony queenless. So they begin to plan for the production of several new queens.

The workers construct special cells in which to raise royalty. Sometimes they enlarge an old worker cell which contains an egg. Sometimes they build completely new cells that jut out from the lower edge of a comb, looking like inch-long fingers with a rough, pitted surface, and with the

opening at the bottom. In such a cell the workers place an egg from a worker cell. In three days the egg hatches and the young larva as usual is fed only royal jelly. This she eats ravenously.

A miraculous development now takes place, making a queen from a worker egg. This is caused, so far as beemen know, by the much roomier cradle and the great amounts of royal jelly the larva consumes. Unlike a worker larva, the queen is fed only royal jelly throughout her life. The queen floats in a pond of it, and laps it up like a glutton. The royal jelly soon becomes gummy so that neither it nor the larva falls from the opening at the bottom of the cell.

As the queen larva develops in her upside-down cradle, her body becomes very different from that of either a worker or a drone. When adult, she will have no tools on her legs, but she will have a sting that she can use again and again, and all the complicated inside organs needed for motherhood.

At the end of 5½ days, the queen larva is ready to be sealed over. Inside the sealed cell her head is against the wax cover. She spends another 7½ days imprisoned in quiet solitude; thus she is about 15 days old when she pulls herself out, a fully formed queen. These periods vary a little, depending on how warm the hive is and the amount of care she receives.

When ready to emerge, the queen cuts with her jaws an almost complete circle in the lid of her cell, as neatly as if done by a can opener. Then she gives the lid a little push, it swings open, and she steps out with beautiful downy body and gauzy wings. Sometimes she is im-

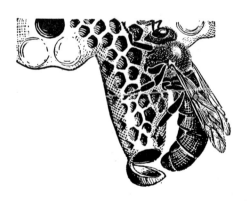

mediately surrounded by workers who caress her, lick her body with their tongues, and comb down her hair. Other times they pay little attention to her at first.

The youthful queen seems at home at once. She takes a sip of honey from a worker's mouth or from a cell, then walks slowly over the comb, followed by her retinue. She has the same assurance that other newly adult bees show. The usual rule is one queen to a colony, although two or more are sometimes found working harmoniously in the same hive. Perhaps the old queen has not yet left to found a new home and several young queens are just about ready to emerge. The first queen to emerge will usually not tolerate any other in her domain. Her first job is to rid herself of rivals.

She begins to look for queen cells and when she finds one well developed she tears at it madly with her jaws. When she has made a hole large enough for her abdomen, she turns, pushes the end of her body into the torn cradle, and kills the inmate with her sting.

Meanwhile the workers look on passively. As

soon as the queen moves to another cell, they drag out the dead body, and finish tearing the cell to pieces.

The queen shows the same fury over other cells containing nearly ready queens, tearing them to pieces and leaving the final destruction to the workers. Sometimes the workers guard two or three queen cells against her, to be sure that the colony will not become queenless. This seems to make the young queen furiously angry and she screams at the rivals that she cannot reach. The sound is called piping but it is really more like "zeep, zeep, zeep." Still in their cells, the rivals reply with a taunting, smothered "quahk! quahk! quahk!" These sounds hurled back and forth are produced, it is thought, by movements of small plates on the wing bases, and are not at all like the usual buzz or hum of bees.

If two queens emerge at the same time, or the old queen is still present, the new queen seeks out her enemy, and they fight to the death, wrestling, biting, trying to find a place to insert the sting. The workers look on like an audience at a prize fight, not interfering, seemingly not caring who wins. The stronger will be their queen.

After the young queen has dusted off all possible rivals, and her helpers have groomed and fed her, she is ready to venture outside. Her first flights are short circles around and around the hive, with her head always pointing toward her home. She is fixing in her mind the location of the hive so that when she goes out for her mating flight, she will be able to find her way back. Then some sunny, warm day, with not too much wind, comes her great moment. This time she bolts out of the hive in a purposeful manner. She rises in larger and larger circles, with all the drones in the neighborhood chasing after her.

The mating over, she crawls into the hive where the workers eagerly await her arrival. It was thought until recently that a queen mated only once in a lifetime, but it is now known that she may take two or three mating flights before settling down to the business of egg-laying.

The queen now moves to the middle part of the hive and starts at once to lay eggs. She will keep up this continuous labor for three or four years and some queens have remained active for as long as seven years.

The queen begins laying in cells a little above the center of a comb in the very middle of the hive; and, moving in ever widening circles, she lays her eggs first on one side of that comb, then on the other. Then she crawls to the next comb and again begins work in the center, always laying in a spiral, first on one side, then on the other.

The central part of the hive is known as the brood nest. At the very center are sealed cells containing pupae. In the neighboring cells are younger larvae, and finally out nearer the edges of the frames, the newly laid eggs. Cells near the outer part of the hive are conveniently filled

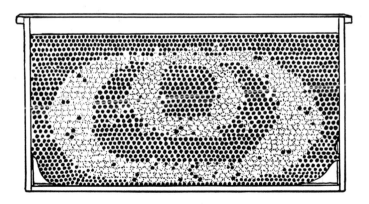

with pollen and honey for the nurse bees to use.

Wherever she goes, the queen has a circle of about a dozen workers around her, all of them with heads turned toward her. Individuals in this circle change often, but she is never left alone. When she wants to eat, she only has to stick out her tongue and one of the workers opens her mouth. The queen puts her tongue in and sucks up some royal jelly. If the first bee she begs from has no jelly ready, the queen turns to another and another until she finds one who has.

Other bees wash her body by lapping her with their tongues, or comb her hairs with their toothed jaws. When she stops to rest or to eat, some of them tap her gently with their antennae as if to show their affection. Of course we cannot know that this is the reason for this action, but that is what it looks like to human eyes.

Ahead of the queen, the busy housekeepers have cleaned out and polished cells for the reception of eggs. When they are through, the queen examines each cell for herself. She sticks her head down into one and, finding it prepared, turns around and thrusts the end of her body all the way to the bottom, her legs holding on to the edges of other cells.

In this crouching position the queen remains for a few seconds as she deposits an egg from the tip of her abdomen. If the cell is one of smaller size, about ⅕ inch across, the queen opens the sac in which the drone has placed sperm, and allows sperm to escape. This little bit of life-quickening substance attaches itself to an egg as the egg slips past the opening of the sac. This egg will become a worker bee.

If the queen finds herself over a larger, drone cell, about ¼ inch across, she withholds the sperm. This egg will develop into a drone. The queen examines each cell with head and anten-

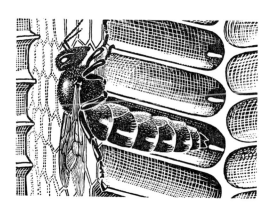

nae before turning about and laying an egg. This goes on, hour after hour, day after day.

If you look into the bottom of a cell visited by the queen you will see that the egg, about the size of a coarse grain of sand, is glued to the exact center of the bottom of the cell, from which it sticks out at an angle, white and glistening. Every egg is slanted in the same direction.

A queen may lay more than 3500 eggs a day, more than her own weight, but the average rate is from 1500 to 2000 a day at the height of a honey flow in summer. How happy a poultryman would be if his hens could lay at that rate!

As spring advances, all the field bees in the colony speed up their work, for the fields and woods are full of food for the taking. The queen feels the same urge for speed. She lays more and more eggs as the honey flow increases. Then in August, when the flowering season is coming to a close, she, as well as the workers, slows her pace.

A queen's days would seem to be very dull. But sometimes, in early spring, she may have her chance for excitement if a swarm leaves the colony. A swarm is a group of field bees who decide to migrate to a new home, taking a queen with them. The queen may be the old one, or one newly hatched.

Maybe the colony contains so many young adults that the hive is crowded. Maybe there is no longer space for brood-raising. Maybe the colony is out of balance in some other way as yet unknown. Whatever the cause, the hum of contentment is gone. When bees are getting ready to swarm, they move restlessly over the comb and they build queen cells. They provide these cells so that the bees left behind will not long be queenless.

The members of the family who remain in the old home are young adults, all the pupae, larvae, and eggs, and the workers who missed the fun by being in the field when the swarm left.

Old bee masters used to say, "A swarm of bees in May is worth a load of hay; a swarm of bees in June is worth a silver spoon; a swarm of bees in July isn't worth a fly."

If a swarm left in May, the old beekeeper thought himself lucky, that is, if he were able to catch it. He then had two colonies instead of one. There was still time for both to grow strong before any heavy flow of nectar occurred. In June, there was less time for the two colonies to build up to greatest strength in field bees for gathering the nectar. Both parts of the split colony would need time to develop eggs into adults. That's why the best part of the gathering season would be over if the swarm did not issue until July. It wouldn't be worth a fly.

When a colony swarms, it is as if most of the field workers went out on strike, leaving behind the inexperienced hands and brood of no use until grown up. If the swarm left the old queen, she might be past her prime.

So the beekeeper of today says, "No swarm in any month is best." When he sees signs of restlessness and finds queen cells prepared, he immediately gives the colony plenty of empty comb in the supers and cuts out the queen cells.

The usual time for a swarm to leave is in the middle of the day, from about ten until two o'clock, and it is one of the most thrilling sights to be seen in an apiary. First, a strange deep hum

is heard inside and some bees come pushing out the entrance and run up the front of the hive. Others dash out and take to the air immediately with a loud buzz.

Then a mob is boiling out the door and the air is suddenly full of bees darting like points of light this way and that, as if they were excitedly trying to find out where to go. Soon they gather closer and now they look like a summer cloud blown by the wind. If trees are nearby, they may begin to gather on a limb; and, if the queen is with them, they hang together, clinging to each other, with lifted abdomens that send out an odor that seems to call, "Come here, we've got the queen!"

More and more join the cluster, then they quiet down and soon, looking like a huge bunch of grapes, the whole mass is quiet. The beekeeper hopes they will cluster somewhere in the bee yard so that he can lure them into a hive. Swarming bees rarely sting, partly perhaps because they are too full of honey.

Next, a few bees on the outside of the bunch leave. These are the scouts who will hunt for a suitable place in which to establish a new home.

Sometimes scouts leave the hive before the swarm; and, if they have found a nice hollow tree or sheltered cave, they lead the others directly to it. But more frequently the crowd waits patiently for the news brought by many scouts who go off in different directions.

Recently a scientist published the results of his study of the behavior of these scouts. He found that each one who returns to the hanging swarm dances in a certain way, telling of her find, the direction to take, and the distance to it. Which scout's selection is best? Some seem to defer to others who have found a better location, and they give up their dance to copy that of one of their mates. Maybe twenty will then join in the same dance on the outer surface of the swarm, apparently saying, "We agree—this sister has found the choice site—let's go!" But on the other side of the cluster, twenty others may be dancing in a different way! Here are two groups each pulling for what they think is best. The majority wins! The swarm waits until there is agreement and all scouts are doing the same dance. Then off they go for the chosen home.

Many beekeepers clip the wings of a queen so that, if she attempts to go out with a swarm, she cannot fly. She may tumble to the ground near the hive where the beeman finds her with a few loyal workers about her. He knows that the swarm will return when they find they are without the queen. To entice them back, he puts a new hive where the earlier home was. This one contains plenty of empty comb and a few combs of brood. He encloses the queen in a little wire cage so that she cannot get away, and adds that to the new home. Winging back come the wanderers to find their queen. A few drop to the

alighting board and whiff her scent. They immediately signal to the others by fanning their wings and giving off an odor that seems to say, "Come on home! Our queen is here!"

Then they begin to push into the entrance in a great crowd, to find that, strange to say, they have plenty of empty comb, and lots of work to do! Whether they wonder what happened in the short time they were away we'll never know, but they settle down contentedly and take up their usual duties. Soon the beekeeper releases the queen and all is well. He has not lost a big group of field bees.

The hive from which the swarm has issued has been removed to another location. The queen in her roomy quarters, with cells waiting to be filled with eggs, settles again to her routine. When plants are not furnishing much nectar and pollen, she stops her frenzied speed and takes it easy. But if another great honey flow begins to come in, she speeds up her activity. With the coming of fall, egg-laying nearly stops. But new bees will be needed throughout the winter to take the place of those who die, and many will be needed for the rush of spring work. So during the winter the queen sticks to her task.

But there comes a time when the queen realizes that she is old and less able to carry on her duties. The workers may realize it too and then they rear new queens. The old queen's life does not end like that of a worker, who works up to the last minute. Her death is more tragic than that. Often she will be found crawling slowly out of the entrance, walking to the edge of the alighting board and tumbling off to die of starvation in the grass. But if some worker finds her, she is not allowed to linger. The worker sends out the word, and others gather about their queen. Now they do not stroke her, nor feed her. Instead they pull at her wings and legs until she is badly injured; then, instead of stinging her to death, they "ball" her. That is, they gather in a great ball around her, pressing closer and closer, until she is smothered. This may take place inside the hive before she has a chance to crawl away. But workers never sting a queen. In killing her, they have as usual put the good of the colony above all else; it's the law of the hive.

10. *Field Bees at Work*

WHAT would life be like in your neighborhood if we had no community, state, and federal governments? You can imagine the difficulties you would be in. For example, think what life would be like if we had no traffic laws; if every driver could go at any speed he liked, on either side of the road, with no signals or stops at intersections. The loss of life would be so terrific that someone would surely rise up and say, "Let's make some laws!"

If you lived alone on an island you could do exactly as you pleased, but when you live near others, you need to consider them as well as yourself, and some sort of rules of conduct must be made. We delegate responsibility to elected persons to make and carry out our laws, and to others to punish lawbreakers.

Bees seem to be completely different. Thousands of them live together, yet they have no visible governing body. All the control of conduct is inside the individual bee. Of course if each human being would always do what is best for everyone else, as bees do, we too should need no laws and no jails.

Bees cannot reason as we do. They are like wound-up machines that always act in the same way toward an outside force acting upon them. Beemen say that their colonies often show distinct personalities, one being nervous and excitable, another calm and gentle, yet in general their behavior is always "predictable."

You have already learned that if you startle a bee she will sting; if you give a colony empty cells, they will be filled with nectar, no matter how great the supply already carried in. If a colony is overcrowded, it will swarm; if the temperature of the hive is low, the members of the family will huddle in a ball to keep themselves warm.

Worker bees do all the work; members of a colony do not interfere with one another but cooperate and help one another.

Indeed, the keynote of success in the life of the hive seems to be cooperation. This is shown clearly in the work of the field bees. They are the workers who change from house duties to outdoor tasks when about three weeks old. No more inside chores for them, except in emergencies. They are now field bees. The fuzzy hairs covering their eyes have dropped off, the glands in the head no longer supply royal jelly, their wax glands no longer make wax. They are now ready for the far heavier duty of providing supplies for the growth, development, and comfort of the colony.

Field bees first try a few test flights to make sure they have the location of their home well in mind. Then they begin carrying in the four necessities of bee life: water, nectar, pollen, and propolis. Outdoor workers do not specialize in collecting only one kind of food; a bee that is a water carrier today may gather pollen or nectar tomorrow. But if a worker begins to collect from a certain source, she sticks to that source until the supply gives out. So when clover nectar begins to appear in the combs, the beekeeper can count on pure clover honey until the clover flow dries up.

Before many bees fly to any source of food, a few scouts go out early in the morning to locate a spot where plenty can be found. These scouts or searchers save time for the main force of workers by telling them in which direction to go and what they will find there. It is probable that after a scout has told the good news she then becomes a field worker.

In early spring the first necessity is water. Probably a little water is taken into a hive every day in the year, except in the tropics, where much more is always needed to cool the hive. This activity is not noticeable in cooler climates except in early spring when the nurse bees need water badly to dilute the thick honey and pollen held in the hive during the winter.

A scientist watched water carriers making their first flights after a colony had been held indoors by wintry weather for 45 days. He caught about two dozen of the incoming bees as they reached the alighting board and pressed their abdomens gently as he held the bees over filter paper. Out came water. When let loose, the carriers hurried into the hive and performed the dance that told their comrades what they had brought in. (The dance will be described in another chapter.)

Four or five bees followed each dancer and she gave them small sips from her load; then, "elbowing her way through the crowd . . . in a business-like fashion," she danced again and transferred the rest of the water she had to other bees.

Next the water carrier made ready for another trip to the water supply. She ate a little, either taking food from a house bee's mouth or honey from a cell. Before making a start to the field, she "almost invariably gives her tongue a swipe between her front feet, rubs her eyes, and often cleans her antennae. She takes a quick look around, then hurries off."

Some of the bees that have followed the water carrier now fly to the water source, and, returning, they perform the same dance that the first one did. Since a mild day in early spring may be followed by several wintry ones, the colony will need enough water to carry over from one mild day to the next. This seems to be the reason that more is carried in than can be used immediately. Of course, it must be stored somewhere, and the resourceful bees draft some of the house bees to act as "water jugs." The water is transferred to their honey sacs until their abdomens are so distended the poor bees can scarcely move. They remain quiet on the comb until, little by little, they give up the water as needed and take up other duties.

Later, when days become hot and dry, many water carriers are in the field because water is needed for cooling the hive. The brood chamber must be kept at a temperature around 93 degrees. The beekeeper helps by providing shade and seeing that the apiary is close to water. A

shallow brook will do or even a pail of water covered with burlap that dips a little below the surface. The bees stand on the burlap and suck up the water with no danger of drowning. Bees prefer their water warm.

How bees know enough to devise a cooling system is a mystery, but they are efficient engineers in air conditioning and are usually able to keep the hive from becoming overheated. They spread the water over the greatest possible area and evaporate it in the following unique way.

The water carriers parcel out the water they have in their honey sacs to a group of indoor bees standing near them, who in turn share it with others. Next, those having a small quantity carry the water to the part of the hive where there are capped cells. Here each one opens her jaw over the slight depressions between cell cappings and deposits a tiny drop. Similar pools are sometimes placed in shallow cups made from old comb on the top bars.

Where there are uncapped cells, especially those containing an egg or a larva, a bee crawls upside down in a cell, produces a droplet from her mouth, and spreads it thinly over the upper cell wall. Sometimes a droplet can be seen hanging there.

Then, after the water is so distributed, the last step in the cooling system is the fanning. By fanning their wings, other workers evaporate the water and thus lower the hive's temperature.

Another method of cooling through evaporation is followed by a number of bees who appear idle but who are, on close inspection, quite busy. They unfold their tongues a little, close them, unfold them a little more, fold them back again, unfold them still further, and then hold them there for one or two seconds. A drop of liquid

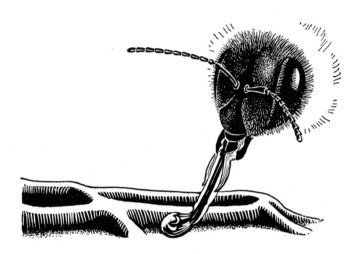

appears between the mouth parts and, by the movement, is drawn into a film which quickly evaporates. Here again the final step is the fanning. The workers manage to create a draft that enters the hive from one side of the entrance and goes out the other side.

The work of both inside and outside bees here fits together nicely as usual. Somehow the indoor bees make it known that water is needed. The water carriers bring it back promptly and hand it over, then go out for more. The indoor bees share it, then spread their portion or evaporate it from their tongues, and finally the fanners take over.

Nectar and pollen gathering begin with the

blooming of the first flowers of spring. Nectar and pollen are the two foods of bees. Pollen is often called "bee bread." It contains highly nutritious proteins and other substances needed for growth. Nectar is made up mostly of sugars that provide energy. To the nectar the bee adds substances from its own body.

The greatest amount of pollen of the season is gathered from blooming trees. Willow twigs are covered with "pussies"; elder trees, elms, and maples hang out their tassels; and fruit trees become big bouquets of colored blossoms.

Every time a bee enters a flower she is likely to push her hairy body against the stamens. The stamens hold the powdery pollen. Pollen is the male element needed by the plant to fertilize the seed. Seed will not develop unless some pollen reaches the pistil. The pistil is the organ at the bottom of which the seed grows. As the bee flies from flower to flower, she brushes against the sticky tip of the pistil and some of the pollen she is carrying rubs off. In this way, the bee does a very important job and, without knowing it, pays for the food she takes away.

When a bee's body becomes heavy with pollen she may stop to brush it off and pack her pollen baskets, or she may do this while flying. With her first pair of legs, she brushes it from her head and

takes moistened pollen from her mouth. The second pair clean the clinging grains from the thorax. The back legs collect the pollen from the hairy abdomen. All of it is moistened before being packed away in the pollen baskets for the rest of the journey home.

Many scientists have watched marked bees

collecting nectar in the field. One scientist spent hours and hours in one spot watching the bees come and go. He marked certain ones and watched for their return. He found that a field bee worked on one clover head until she had pushed her tongue down to the bottom of almost every small floret, and in so doing brushed her hairy body against the other florets. The bee would then fly home, but the watcher would stay on the alert for her return. It would be some time

before he could spot her again on a nearby flower, and he was able to discover that each bee works over just a small area. She makes the first flower the center of a spiral, gradually widening her circles. The area covered in a patch of dandelions was 30 feet by 17 feet when "the patch had a fair population of blossoms," but increased to 61 feet by 25 feet when the flowers were farther apart. A bee on alsike clover gathered in only a small spot, eight feet by nine feet in size. "Five bees," the watcher said, "remained faithful visitors of buckwheat and aster plots for 25 days, and one other for 23 days."

How many trips a day one bee can make as a gatherer, he concluded, depends on the weather, the distance from the hive, the amount of time spent on one blossom, the amount of nectar flow, and the like. But the possible trips per day may range from seven to ten on alsike clover, four to six on buckwheat, three to nine on goldenrod, and six to eight on dandelion. A bee working over a small area, before she takes off for home, usually returns to the plant that she had started on.

It has been calculated that a minimum of two pounds of nectar is required to make one pound of honey. Most nectars contain less than 50 per cent sugar. A bee that makes ten trips to the field a day would carry in about ⅟₇₅ pound of nectar during a twenty-day period. No wonder so many bees are required to obtain the surplus a bee-keeper wants for himself. It is assumed that a colony containing about 60,000 bees would be able to put about 20,000 in the field for gathering.

Three thousand bees, according to one student of bees, could bring in enough nectar in a day to produce one pound of ripe honey. It is not unusual for a beekeeper to take off as much as 200 pounds of honey from one hive during a single season and still leave enough for the needs of the colony during the winter.

The job of producing honey from nectar is not over when the nectar is brought into the hive. It still has to be changed from a watery liquid into the ripened honey. When a heavy honey flow is on, with more flowers offering their sweet than the field bees can gather, the collectors do not take the time to carry their loads to cells and deposit the nectar there. Instead they deliver it to house bees by opening their jaws and bringing up from the honey sac the nectar they have swallowed. A house bee puts her tongue between the jaws of the gatherer and sucks up a drop. As they make this exchange, the antennae of the two bees gently tap each other on the face.

The house bee who receives the liquid holds it for about twenty minutes while she stands motionless facing the top of the hive, working the nectar over in her mouth and honey sac. She swings out her proboscis a little, then brings it back, opens it wider, and shuts it again. After five or ten seconds the bee swallows the drop, only to bring it up again and go through the same motions once more. Some of the water in the nectar is thus evaporated, and chemicals from glands in the mouth and honey sac have been added.

Next, the house bee carries this unripe honey, now thickened and changed chemically, to an empty cell and deposits it there. She crawls in upside down so that she faces the ceiling wall of the cell. Then using her mouth parts as a brush, she swish-swashes the unripe honey across the upper wall. It either hangs as a drop there or runs down toward the bottom.

The droplets become thicker as the water in them evaporates. The chemicals change the sugar in the original nectar into the most easily digested sugar in the world. When the bees are aware that the honey is thick enough, they cover the filled cells with a lid of wax, and there the honey will keep indefinitely.

When frames are filled with the sealed sweetness, the beekeeper takes them out and gives the bees empty combs to refill. He still has work to do if he expects to sell the honey in liquid form. He cuts off the sealing layer of wax with a warm knife or a machine, and puts the frames into an extractor. This is a machine that, by whirling the open honeycomb, drives out the honey, leaving the empty cells. Before he bottles it he must filter out any debris. Bottled honey is clear and sparkling, ranging in color from water-white to pale amber to dark amber, depending on the kind of flower from which the bees gathered the nectar.

Propolis is the sticky gum found on the bark of some trees and plants, and on some buds. Bees use it as glue to seal all cracks in the hive through which wind or water might enter. This, the least important of the outside materials brought into a colony, can be gathered only when it is warm enough for the gum to be pliable so that the bees can pull it away. It may be gathered at any time needed during the summer, but most of it is carried in during early fall.

How the bees gather this resinous tough substance has been described by a scientist who saw a bee alight on a tree trunk close to a drop of gum and tear at it with her jaws. The gluey substance strung out, and it was only after repeated efforts that she was able to tear off a piece. This she placed in her pollen baskets, using her middle pair of legs to do so. She kept at that gum, tearing and pulling, until her pollen baskets were full.

When she arrived home with her trophy, other bees gathered round and removed the glue, pulling and hauling her this way and that as they tried to get it out. At last she was free to clean herself up, take a snack of honey, and go out for more. The indoor bees carried the propolis to the spot where it was needed to fill a crack or chink through which cold winds might enter. Often bees will glue the cover of the hive down tight, so that a beekeeper who wishes to open the hive must use his hive tool to gently pry the lid off.

Sometimes propolis is used by bees to cover unwanted objects that are too heavy for them to carry outside. For example, a field mouse may wander through the entrance. Instantly it will be stung to death, but there is the problem of a dead body to dispose of. The best the bees can do is cover it with glue and let it lie on the bottom board, where they must walk around and over the huge lump.

Some races of honeybees use more propolis than do others. The violin varnish used by the old Italian makers of the finest violins was largely made up of propolis gathered by bees from poplar tree trunks.

11. *Fall and Winter*

WHEN fall comes, nectar and pollen are harder to find, for the blooming season is nearly at an end. At this time, particularly if warm weather lingers, some bees turn to robbing to fill their hives for winter. They try to creep into a crack in some other hive or make a bold dash for the entrance. A weak colony may not be able to fight off the thieves and more and more of their honey will be stolen.

A beekeeper knows when robbing is going on.

He sees the quick dart of the robbers, their dragging legs on the alighting board, unlike the sure entrance of a homing bee. From the robbed colony comes a sound very different from the contented hum of an undisturbed hive. The shrill excited buzzing is a cry for help to his ears. He then makes the entrance small so that fewer guards are needed to keep out the marauders and opens the hives only when absolutely necessary.

Bees that once begin robbing seem to develop the habit and soon the thieves become dark and thin, nervous, and old looking. The hairs of their body have been torn off in fights with policemen or worn off by trying to creep through narrow crevices. Evidently crime does not pay among bees!

Many field bees die in harness toward the end of the season. They literally work themselves to death in the service of the colony, often dropping dead as they carry in one last load. Their fuzz has worn off, their wings have become frayed, and their span of life has been a bare six or seven weeks. So in late fall most of the field bees are dead, others will die during the cold season. The drones are all dead and the queen stops egg-laying. The colony now consists of a few larvae, young bees that have not yet flown, field bees born in late summer, and the queen. About 30,-000 bees make up a winter colony.

At home, when winter comes, you put away your bat and baseball, and begin to think of sleds, skates, and skis. Your father starts the furnace so that your house will be warm no matter what the outside temperature is. You begin to wear an overcoat and mittens. Many birds fly to a warm climate. Bears, snakes, and other animals curl up in some protected spot and sleep through the winter. Most insects are safe as eggs or in cocoons. Bees, too, have a way of keeping themselves warm inside the hive.

The beekeeper now pays his little partners for all the honey he has taken from them during the summer. He sees that they have plenty of honey and pollen to last them through the winter. He blocks the entrance so that cold winds cannot enter yet the bees can get out if a warm day comes along. He makes a special top entrance (a small augur hole), and then he wraps the hive in insulating material to protect it from wind.

The good beekeeper leaves from 40 to 60 pounds of honey and from three to five frames of pollen in the combs. He also returns to the hive the pollen which had been scraped off the back legs of homecoming bees into a pollen trap during the honey season. He may even add soybean flour to the pollen to make sure his bees have enough to eat during the winter, and for brood-raising in early spring.

Bees are cold-blooded animals; that is, their body temperature is the same as that of the outside air. If it is 80 degrees outside, the bee's body will register 80; if it falls to 70, the bee's temperature falls too. When the temperature goes lower than 50 degrees, a bee cannot fly; at

45 degrees it cannot move; and below 32 it slowly freezes to death. For centuries it has been known that when the temperature falls below a certain point, the bees huddle in a ball in the center of the hive, clustering over the cells and between the combs. Then in 1914, two American scientists discovered exactly what happens in that huddle. They made a hive with glass sides so that they could watch and put tiny thermometers into every part of the hive and in the middle of the ball.

When the temperature fell to 57 degrees, the bees began to huddle but not many joined the cluster until the air temperature dropped to about 43 to 46 degrees. Then, the lower the thermometer registered outdoors, the higher it registered inside the winter cluster. The bees were manufacturing their own heat. The outer layer of the cluster was like the rind of an orange and was composed of individuals standing quietly side by side with their heads turned inward. With their hairy bodies touching, they formed a perfect layer of insulation. Within this living blanket, the bees became active as soon as the temperature fell to 45 degrees. The colder it grew outside, the greater their activity. Every empty cell contained a bee tucked in head first, her posterior protruding. The rest of them were wiggling; antennae waved, abdomens wagged, wings fanned, and the harder they waved and

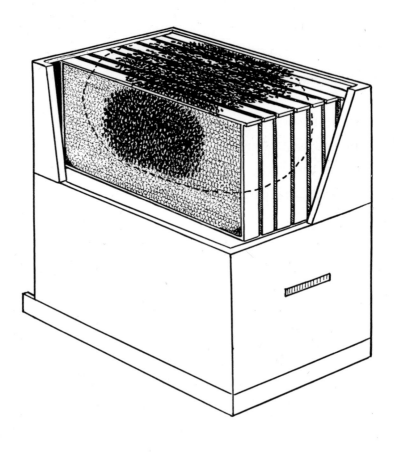

wagged and fanned, the higher the temperature rose.

They were doing just what we do when we wait in the cold on the corner for a late bus: moving arms, legs, feet to create heat by muscular energy. There is precision in the way the bees do this work, each taking a shift as gymnastic heat producer. Muscular energy must be renewed by food; and, as the activity in the cluster increases, more trips are made to the honey stores. To prevent the bees from using up too much energy and eating too much honey, the beekeeper provides a blanket of shavings or tar paper to keep the hive warm. If he is successful, he finds in the spring, not only the honey which the bees did not have to eat, but young fresh bees not frazzled from a winter of hard labor. The bees in the insulating layer have to endure the cold, and often these faithful soldiers die at their posts.

When the heat in the cluster reaches about 93 degrees, the queen begins laying eggs again, and brood rearing continues until spring if the bees have enough stores to feed the larvae.

12. *The Language of Bees*

WHEN you want to speak to someone, you usually use words made up of sounds that you form with your lips, tongue, and throat. But sometimes you talk without words—you may shake your head for "no" or "yes," you may smile to show pleasure, or frown and pout at something you dislike. If someone is too far away to hear you speak, you may wave your arm in a curve that means "Come here!"

That is the kind of language used by bees, the

language of body motion. They also have another way of speaking by means of odors. For many years it was unknown how one bee told another where to go to find food. Then Dr. Karl von Frisch of Germany found out the secret of bees' language. In 1949 he crossed the Atlantic Ocean and lectured at Cornell University on the results of his many years of experiments. He made a hive in which the frames of comb were placed end to end instead of hanging parallel. Each frame was covered with glass on both sides so that the bees could be observed at work. He numbered the bees so that he could recognize them by putting a dab of paint—using five different colors—on different parts of the body.

Here are some of the amazing facts Dr. von Frisch found out: Early in the morning a few scouts flew out to search for nectar. As each scout left, Dr. von Frisch gave her a dab of paint. When she returned, she climbed on a comb and was immediately surrounded by her sisters. To each one she gave a bit of her nectar, touching her tongue to their outstretched ones. They paid close attention, touching her with their antennae.

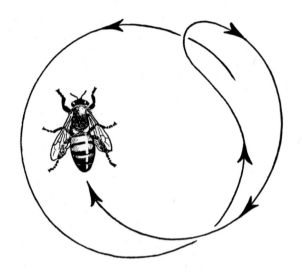

Then she stood on one spot and began turning, once to the right, once to the left, in a whirling figure eight. She did this for half a minute. Then she moved to another spot on the comb and repeated her round dance. She was telling them first, when she gave them a taste of the nectar, "I've found lots of this nectar—go out and help bring it in." If the flower from which she had gathered had fragrance, some of that odor would cling to her body and the antennae of the surrounding bees would tell them what odor to look for.

Her dancing also told them that the source of nectar was nearby. The bees who crowded near became excited. They touched her again and again. And then they flew out of the hive. Dr. von Frisch tested the bees over and over, and discovered that they invariably came back with the same kind of nectar the scouts had.

Dr. von Frisch also discovered scouts dancing in a different way—a wagging dance that told their sisters, "There's lots of this nectar to be had, but it's more than half a mile away in that direction." This sounds incredible, doesn't it? The

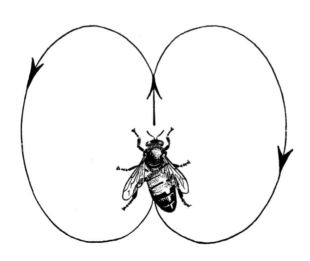

dance consisted of wagging the whole back part of the body as they took a few running steps in a straight line. Then they made a complete turn to the left, repeated the wag-wag steps, and made another complete turn to the right. This pattern was repeated over and over and over again. It was the straight-line run that told the bees in what direction to fly. The wag meant the flowers were far away.

The dancing bee makes her running steps straight to the top of the hive if the bees are to fly directly into the sunshine. If she goes to the right or left, they are to fly at that angle away from the sun. If they are to fly directly away from the sun, she turns her running steps toward the bottom of the hive.

The strangest part of all is that even though the sun may be behind clouds, the bees, by a sixth sense which we do not have, are able to locate themselves correctly with regard to the position of the sun.

Direct light from the sun vibrates equally in all directions, and light scattered by particles in the atmosphere vibrates more in some directions than in others. We say that such light is "polar-ized." The direction in which the light vibrates shows the position of the sun, and bees are sensi-tive to this vibration. In the dark, the bees' sense of direction is lost, for their "direction finder" or "light compass" responds only to sunlight which is present to some extent even when the weather is cloudy.

Some flowers that contain food for bees do not have fragrance. How then can the foraging bees find the right flowers when they have gone about the right distance in the right direction? That too has been discovered. The first bees to find those flowers send out a special odor from their bodies that says, "This way! Here are the flowers you're looking for!" The bees flying above catch the scent and drop to blossoms nearby. This special body odor is kept in a tiny pocket at the end of the abdomen and is used only for this purpose.

The language of odor is used often and is very effective. In fact, one might say that it is odor which holds a family of bees together. Every bee is well equipped with organs of smell in glands on the forward portion of the antennae. They serve not only to locate fragrant flowers, but to recognize hive mates, queen, and enemies. The antennae also have organs of touch. A round scented object may give a different sensation to a bee from that of an angular one. Hence, both touch and smell are useful to bees as they visit a flower. Different parts of some flowers may have different scents, and one special odor on the part of the flower leading to the nectar may guide the bee to that spot.

Long ago, a scientist distinguished seven different odors in a colony, to which a bee responds. These are odors of (1) the individual, (2) the children of one queen, (3) the brood and larvae, (4) the drone, (5) the wax, (6) the honey, and (7) the hive. The hive odor is a combination of all or some of the others. Even with our rather poor sense of smell, we can detect the different odors of wax, honey, and hive.

The individual's own scent seems to be produced by a gland on the upper surface of the abdomen in the soft membrane between two of the overlapping hard rings. In times of swarming,

when the scouts have found a suitable place for the new home, they stand with their abdomens raised and these glands exposed. At the same time they fan their wings furiously to diffuse the scent. This odor can be detected by anyone not afraid to put his nose close to the fanning bees. All beekeepers know that swarming bees seldom sting. They seem to have lost their urge to sting or are too busily occupied with other matters. Also, they have gorged themselves with honey enough to last them a few days and their abdomens are so swollen with it that they can't very easily push out the sting.

The sense of smell is important in detecting enemies and sneak thieves. The guards are usually on the alert and let no one past without submitting her to the odor test. If the incoming bee has the family hive odor or if she carries a load of food, she is allowed in, otherwise she is attacked, stung to death, and dragged outside. Wasps and bumblebees are treated in the same way. Occasionally a lizard or a mouse forces its way in, but the guards set upon it ferociously and the giant-size enemies are soon conquered and stung to death.

Whether the bees' sense of hearing is developed is not yet known, but some of the pits and glands in various parts of the body may be hearing organs. It is true that bees make plenty of different sounds, but, then, so can a totally deaf man.

A beekeeper can interpret the noises made by his pets. The one he likes best to hear is the contented hum of a busy colony. Then there is the excited swarm tone of bees who leave their old home for a new one; the buzz of a colony being robbed; the sounds made by a queen; and the lamenting tone when a colony becomes queenless. When a new queen is introduced, this changes to a loud welcoming buzz.

13. *Other Kinds of Bees*

HONEYBEES belong to the family of insects named Apidae. They are cousins, so to speak, of the ants (Formicidae) and wasps (Vespidae). Among the Apidae are some bees that are useful to the farmer for pollination, but they do not live in large colonies so they cannot do the great amount of good that honeybees do. Nevertheless, they should be protected.

The bumblebee is a wonderful pollinator for crops that honeybees do not touch because their tongues are not long enough to reach to the bottom of the flower cups where the nectar is found. Bumblebees are much larger than honeybees and their tongues are longer.

In the spring a queen bumblebee that has lived over the winter crawls out of her last year's nest and hovers over the ground looking for a cozy little hole to start her new family in. Often this is a nest left by a field mouse. The bumblebee now gathers nectar and pollen and mixes them together into a loaf about the size of a mar-

ble. Upon this source of food she lays a few eggs. The larvae that hatch burrow into the loaf, eating their fill. A few wax cells are made for them to pupate in. When the pupae become adults, they are worker bees, who make new burrows in the nest for more bee bread. They also strengthen with wax the cells they have left and store honey in them. All the eggs laid in spring and early summer become worker bees. Then in late summer more queens and some drones are developed. But when winter arrives, all the inmates of the nest die except the queens, which seem to be hardier than the rest.

Another relative of the honeybee is the carpenter bee. You can often see its nest if you break a twig of sumac or elder in the spring. Inside where the pith was, you will find a tunnel divided into small cells, one above the other, separated by partitions made of sawdust glued together. A wasp makes a similar tunnel, but it uses mud to separate the cells, and the food placed in each cell will be bits of dead insects, while the carpenter bee uses pollen and nectar mixed together. The mother bee lays an egg in

each little room, placing it on top of the food. When the larva has passed through the pupal stage and is ready to emerge, it chews its way upward through the partition. In the cell above it joins with the next bee and they cut their way from one room to the next, meeting other bees, until all are at the top. Then out they all go together through the hole the mother has left in the twig.

The leaf-cutting bee is also a relative of the honeybee. She makes a tube in old wood for her nest. She lines the tube with pieces of rose leaf or pansy petal, making a series of cells like

those of the carpenter bee, only much more beautiful. The cells are separated by circular bits of leaf or petal that, when tucked in, just fit the tube. She leaves a little food for each baby and the young bees cut their way out cell by cell until they reach the top of the tube.

The small burrowing bee makes a tunnel in the earth with side pockets to hold larvae and stores of food.

The honeybee has some other relatives with the first name of *Apis*. The bee we have talked about in this book is *Apis mellifica*. The others,

Apis dorsata, a giant bee, and *Apis florea,* a dwarf bee, live in the Far East. The giant bee of India builds only a single comb in the open air, usually hanging it from a tree. These Eastern bees are not of much use to man.

Besides these different types of bees, we also have different *races* of the honeybee, *Apis mellifica.* Just as we have differences in color of skin and temperament among human beings, we have differences in color and temperament among the various races of honeybees. The bees known as Caucasians, because they were originally found in the Caucasus Mountains, are often gray in color and are very gentle. They use propolis so lavishly that many beekeepers find them a nuisance.

The German race of honeybees is black in color. They are often cross, sting easily, and, since they do not keep their hives clean, are likely to contract a disease known as European foul brood. American beekeepers refuse to raise them.

The Carniolan race from the mountains in Austria is grayish black in color. It has a bad habit of swarming at the least provocation. Otherwise, these bees would probably be highly popular with beekeepers.

The Italian race is the favorite with American beekeepers because it combines all the good qualities. Italian bees have alternate yellow and black bands across their bodies; they are fairly gentle, are excellent honey gatherers, and do not swarm readily. Therefore they have endeared themselves to beekeepers and are now known as the "standard" bees of America.

14. *Plants That Bees Visit*

A FARMER cultivates hay and grain for his livestock, or he buys feed for his chickens, geese, turkeys, and pigs. A beekeeper is free from all this labor and expense. What he does is to choose a location for his apiary where nectar-bearing plants are abundant. The nearer they are to the apiary the better. The bees forage for themselves. Yet choosing an apiary site is not a simple matter for the beekeeper. A plant that secretes nectar in quantity in one part of the

126

country may not do so in another. He must consider too whether, even though a major cultivated crop is available, enough wild plants and trees are near enough to supply the colonies before and after the main honey flows are over.

Each kind of plant yields its greatest amount of nectar on a certain kind of soil. For example, clovers grown on limestone soils in temperate climates are good nectar producers. And large buckwheat honey crops can be obtained when the buckwheat is grown on acid, light, sandy soils in the northeast. Sweet clover produces its best crops in the plains region.

Plants that grow in swamps are often a dependable source for bees because the nectar and pollen do not fail in times of drought. Neither are swamps likely to be plowed when a farmer enlarges his acreage. The blooms from trees are usually dependable too.

Although bees gather from hundreds of different plants, most beekeepers gain their surplus from only a few cultivated crops. One of the greatest sources of honey in the United States is sweet clover, a plant accidentally introduced into this country no one knows when or how. The small white or yellow florets of this three- to five-foot plant are not in a head like those of the low-growing clovers, but are strung out along a three-inch stem. At first sweet clover was considered a weed, but now it has become an important crop for building up the soil. More honey is obtained from it than from any other one source. Clover has spread over the river valleys of the central United States and over the northern plains. The honey that comes from it is a pale clear amber in color and the flavor is mild.

Alfalfa, another great source of honey, is cultivated by farmers as feed for livestock. It grows from 12 to 18 inches tall and the leaf has three parts, as clover leaves have. The florets, violet or blue, are borne on lengthened heads called "short racemes." The honey produced from alfalfa is light in color and delicate in flavor.

Next in importance are the honeys from Dutch white clover and alsike Swedish clover. These low, fragrant plants are cultivated largely east of the Mississippi River as feed for dairy cattle. This honey has a mild flavor and is pale amber in

SWEET
CLOVER

ALFALFA

WHITE CLOVER

color, sometimes almost colorless. Other important bee plants are vetch, cotton, buckwheat, and orange. Most of California's honey crop comes from orange blossoms.

Besides these cultivated crops, many smaller crops of wild plants are useful to bees. The basswood or linden tree was a plentiful source until the cutting of forests made it rare. The same thing has happened to the delicious honey from wild raspberry in northern Michigan and Ontario. Because of intense cultivation of other crops, the wild raspberry is disappearing.

Wild sages—the white, black, and purple varieties—all produce a fine honey that is nearly water-white. Sage honey used to be considered the finest honey on the western coast, but now it is almost impossible to find.

The algaroba tree of Hawaii, called mesquite in Texas, produces large quantities of honey. Its flowers are packed closely on a spike.

One interesting plant that bees find very attractive is fireweed, or willow herb. The delicate pink blossoms of this wild flower often carpet the ugly black wastes after a forest fire.

Hundreds of other plants might be named as important to beekeeping for their nectar and pollen. Their yield may be small and the plants may be scattered widely, but particularly in early spring they help the colonies in their need for food to build the hive population to its greatest strength. Beekeepers try to have their colonies at the peak of fitness when the big honey flows are on from acres and acres of farm crops.

Some of these minor sources are important too in the fall when the big crops are over and the bees still need honey and pollen for winter supplies. Among them are weeds such as heartsease, milkweed, horsemint, goldenrod, aster, and Spanish needle. The dandelion should have special mention for it blooms early and late, produces both pollen and nectar in great quantities, and is found in almost every countryside in America. Tropical plants that are good sources of honey include black mangrove, eucalyptus, acacia, citrus fruits, century plant, hibiscus, thistle, guava, and many others.

Because the ways of farming have changed so greatly in recent years, beemen nowadays sometimes grow their own pasturage, using for crops plants that not only yield honey but give them a profit in other ways. For instance, clover and alfalfa are good cattle feed, and the seed are bought up by seed growers.

In the neighborhood of an apiary some unused land may be going to waste. In such spots it pays the beekeeper to sow the seeds of honey plants. Some beekeepers keep seeds of low-growing plants, such as clover, birdsfoot trefoil, meadow sage, and marjoram, in their pockets to sprinkle along the roadside as they travel. Some may take root and add to the bee pasturage.

In the 1930's Dr. Frank C. Pellett, former Field Editor of the *American Bee Journal*, started a garden of nectar-bearing plants he obtained from other countries. His object was to find new plants that might provide more bee pasture and be valuable to farmers. Of all the plants tried, one from the Caucasus Mountains and the steppes of Russia was most promising. It looks quite like alsike clover, is hardy enough to withstand American winters, and spreads rapidly. It is sometimes called "Pellett clover."

Over the years a beekeeper may find that his major source of honey has disappeared because of changes in the agriculture of his locality. For example, after World War I, sugar beets replaced alfalfa on the eastern slopes of the Rocky Mountains. The same thing happened in the East when farmers turned from growing large fields of buckwheat to other more profitable crops.

Beemen are resourceful, however, and now the removal of an entire apiary from one part of the country to another is quite usual. Many beekeepers have apiaries in the North which they attend to in the summer. Then they go south in the winter to care for the apiaries they keep in a warmer climate, and which will be producing crops of honey there. Or they may move the same bees from North to South, then North again.

The whole subject of honey plants is a large one, and beekeepers find that the more they know about available sources, the better able they are to place their bees where they can take off huge crops of honey.

15. *How Bees Help Farmers*

IF YOU had looked in on a certain farmhouse in upper New York state some ten years ago, you would have seen that Farmer Wayne was deeply worried. He did not know what was wrong. He had owned his 200-acre farm for thirty years, and worked harder every year than the one before, yet his crops grew no larger. In fact, they were poorer, even though he spent more money on sprays, more money on fertilizers. He had bigger fields too, more land under active cultivation. What could be the trouble?

His wife suggested that he go ask the county agricultural agent, but Farmer Wayne couldn't imagine that fellow with a college education knowing as much as he did about farming. At last in desperation, however, he did go to County Agent Morse's office.

Mr. Morse listened to his tale of woe and, when he got through, said:

"Mr. Wayne, you've been killing the goose that lays the golden eggs."

"What do you mean?" asked Farmer Wayne.

"Well, first you cut down the trees in your woods and plowed up all that land, didn't you?"

"Yes, I put it in corn."

"And then you took out all the hedgerows and put in wire fences."

"Sure, I practice clean cultivation—don't waste an inch of ground in weeds if I can help it."

"And then you spray all your land with poisons to kill off the pests."

"That's right—no bug's going to eat my crops."

"But don't you know you kill, besides the pests,

the good insects needed to pollinate most of your crops? Bumblebees, burrowing bees, carpenter bees, flies, ants, butterflies, all are becoming fewer and fewer."

"I thought plants pollinated themselves—don't they?"

"Some do, but most of our food crops—vegetables, fruits, and nuts—need insects to carry the pollen from flower to flower in order for the seeds to develop. You've driven the insects from your woods and destroyed their nests with your plow. You took away hedgerows so that they had no place to nest. Then you killed them off with sprays—no wonder you don't have good crops."

Farmer Wayne's jaw dropped. He thought he knew so much about farming.

"What can I do?" he asked. "I see now why my crops get smaller no matter how hard I work."

"You'll have to do what most farmers in America are learning to do—make a partner of the honeybee."

"How's that again? You mean the bee with the sting?"

"I sure do—the only insect that man can control. Go see a beekeeper and get him to move some of his colonies into your orchards when the trees are blooming. They'll pollinate the blossoms."

Farmer Wayne left the county agent's office a little bewildered. A bee for a partner—that tiny, fuzzy-bodied, gauzy-winged, inch-long buzzer! It was hard to believe, but he guessed he'd try it. Next spring, when the fruit trees were a mass

of bloom, he had a beekeeper move some of his hives in among the trees. Then he watched. Yes, it was easy to see that lots of bees hovered over the trees, then dove into the flowers.

That fall, instead of getting 480 bushels of apples, as he had the year before, his crop was 1580 barrels. And in a couple of years he was getting 2000 barrels.

Farmer Wayne didn't wait after that first trial. He hired those bees to help him with all his crops of vegetables as well as fruits. He discovered that farmers all over the country were doing what he did, either buying their own bees or renting some for pollination.

This has made beekeepers wake up to a new kind of beekeeping. Instead of trying to get large crops of honey and wax to sell, they have found it pays better to build up the number of bees in their apiary and rent or sell colonies to farmers.

"Seems funny," said Farmer Wayne to his wife, "that such a small insect can be an important link in the chain from flowers to crops, from crops to livestock, from livestock to family meals. But, do you know, Sally, our whole system of agriculture depends on the bee! I believe that now."

"Do you mean to tell me that we couldn't have cows without bees?" Sally asked.

"That's what the county agent says. We have to raise more clover and alfalfa seed to feed our cows, and he says if we don't use bees for pollination, in a hundred years we won't have feed for livestock, and may have to do without beef, lamb, pork, milk, butter, and cheese. You wouldn't like to live on rice and fish all your life, would you?"

Well, after that conversation Sally decided to learn how to keep bees herself and pretty soon

she became a first-rate beekeeper. Both she and her husband liked to watch their bees work, and they were pleased when crops got better and better. Then they found that in the years when the apple trees and pear trees bloomed at exactly the same time, the bees preferred the nectar of the apple blossoms, and would fly right over the less-sweet pear trees. What could they do about that? Was there any way in which the bees could be persuaded to pollinate the pear trees? They wrote to the Division of Bee Culture and Biological Control, part of the United States Department of Agriculture, and got the answer.

The answer was that although bees cannot be trained as a dog can, they can sometimes be tricked into pollinating the crop you want them to visit. Experiments of this kind are now going on. What the experimenter does is to put a dish of sugar-and-water sirup and some blossoms of the plant he wants visited inside a hive overnight. Next morning the bees go searching for those flowers. And, as you know, once they start working on a certain kind of plant, they continue to visit it until the nectar is gone. This trick works only when the pear blossoms are in a different direction from the apple. Otherwise the bees are sidetracked by the sweeter apple trees.

The bees that Mrs. Wayne has in her apiary and which most American beemen prefer are the golden-banded gentle Italian race. A few beekeepers like to raise the gray kind because they sting less and are less excitable.

The Waynes found that sometimes their bees got sick, so they had to learn about bee diseases. County Agent Morse was a great help to them. He would come around every little while to see how they were getting along, and he introduced them to the county bee inspector, Mr. Gould.

Once Mr. Gould made Farmer Wayne angry. He told him he would have to burn several of his colonies because they were ill with a disease known as American foul brood.

"It's the law," said Mr. Gould. "If you don't get rid of every bit of this disease in this apiary, it will spread to others in the neighborhood, and soon no beekeeper in this region will have any good colonies."

"Well, what's the matter with curing the disease—doctors treat people with illnesses—they don't burn them up."

"Some bee diseases can be cured, but so far no one has found a cure for American foul brood. Nothing to do but burn every bee and every comb and hive where I find a symptom of it. See here—" He pointed to sunken cells and stuck a toothpick into one. It came out with a long rubbery string of dark substance sticking to it. The larvae in those cells were dead.

"That's a sure sign," he said. "I'm sorry, but we'll have to look at every colony in your apiary. And every infected hive must be burned, bees and all. It's the only safe way to protect the rest of the colonies."

Reluctantly, Farmer Wayne did what the inspector told him. He dug a pit, threw into it every bit of infected material, and had a huge bonfire.

Mrs. Wayne went inside and shut the door. "I just can't bear to see it," she said. "Throwing my pets on that fire—losing all that equipment. It's awful."

So it was, but it was better than losing all their

colonies. They had a few other troubles too. One night they woke up with the smell of a skunk strong in their nostrils. Farmer Wayne got up to shut the window; and, looking out into the moonlight, he saw a skunk among his colonies. It rapped sharply on a hive and, when the bees rushed to the entrance, licked them up and ate them. It didn't take long for the farmer to get his shotgun and take aim. He missed the skunk, but at least it was scared away.

Another time the Waynes returned from a week end away to find the whole apiary in a turmoil. Some large animal had overturned the hives and eaten the combs. Robber bees were sipping up the honey on the ground. When robbers once get a taste of someone else's honey they seem to go crazy. They can't get enough and try to pry their way into every hive. Only the strong colonies can resist them. From the weaker ones came a strong buzz of alarm.

"It was a bear after honey, I'm sure of that," said Farmer Wayne. "And he'll probably come back for more tonight. I'll set a trap." He and his wife spent the day setting things to rights, getting rid of the honey on the ground, giving more bees to the weak colonies so they would be better able to resist the robber bees.

Sure enough, the bear was caught that night, so he gave no more trouble. The Waynes discovered that bees have other enemies, and they became used to losing a few to enemies that could catch them on the wing. Dragonflies, robber flies, toads, some spiders, beetles, wasps, and hornets as well as birds would hang around the apiary and catch as many bees as they could.

Ants are troublesome in the tropics, unless the beekeeper puts his hives on legs and stands the legs in cups filled with oil. The ants can't cross oil. In Hawaii, the hive stand is usually a piece of a log, and the beekeeper puts a band of sticky paper around it to catch ants climbing up.

On the whole, the Waynes had little trouble caring for their bees, and the longer they kept them, the fonder they became of their small partners. Of course they enjoyed the honey too.

If you looked in on that farmhouse today, you would find honey in jars ready to be shipped, and outdoors you would probably find Mrs Wayne in bee veil and gloves taking care of the colonies. Beside the barn they have built a small honey house where the honey is prepared for market. They are doubly repaid for the care they give their bees, in the honey and wax they sell and in the increased crops the bees have made possible.

16. *Would You Like to Keep Bees?*

IF WHAT you have read has made you want to keep bees, here are a few pointers. Fortunately an apiary does not have to be looked after every day in the year. Spring and fall are the seasons when bees need most attention. While you are busiest with schoolwork in the winter, your pets will be quiet inside their hives. Many boys and girls have paid their way through college with the help of their colonies.

For best results—that is, to get large crops of honey and wax, or to obtain large colonies for renting—you will need to know about the ways of bees, something about bee plants, and some of the techniques of beekeeping.

Your 4-H club leader or Scout troop leader may plan a project of beekeeping. Then you'll have the fun of learning about bees with your friends. But the best method is to hunt up a bee-man in your neighborhood and ask him to let you help him in the apiary. Beekeepers are usually enthusiastic about their hobby and are happiest when they can teach someone how to handle bees.

You will need a reference book too. Maybe the state in which you live prints one at its agricultural experiment station. If not, any beekeeper can name a good guidebook or lend you his. The A. I. Root Company, Medina, Ohio, has a small simple book called *Starting Right with Bees.* Another is Addison Webb's *Beekeeping for Profit and Pleasure.* It is a good idea to study a book before you go very far, or to subscribe to one of the beekeeping magazines.

It is best to begin on a small scale by owning from one to five colonies. These you may be able to buy from a beekeeper in the neighborhood, but be sure that his hives have been inspected recently and that he has a certificate showing that his bees are healthy.

Another way to begin is to buy bees by the pound in a package. You can find "Bees for Sale" advertisements in any beekeeping magazine. A three-pound package holds about 9000 bees, enough to start you off with your first hive. Bees are sent through the mail in wire cages, complete with a queen and food for the journey.

Now before making the plunge, you will have to decide where to place your hives, because you want to be sure that the bees can find a plentiful supply of food within a radius of one or two miles. Some city dwellers have been successful keeping their bees in an attic or on a roof, although their bees must travel far for food. You will want your apiary to be more than two miles from another apiary, particularly from the one where you bought your colonies. Otherwise your bees might fly back to their former home.

You will need to shelter your bees from cold north winds in winter. The windbreak may be

a fence or a line of bushes or trees. Also, in summer, if the sun is very hot, the hives need to be shaded.

Suppose you want to keep your colonies in your own backyard, but have fairly close neighbors. Then a hedge or fence is needed to force the bees to fly high and thus avoid contact with passers-by.

Fortunately a beekeeper's equipment is simple and inexpensive. You will need a veil and a hat to protect your head from stings. A commercial veil is usually made of wire screening to cover the face, with a cloth bottom that drops around the neck. The cloth top fits under a hat. A hat is really needed in the apiary, otherwise a bee will surely get in your hair.

You will also need a hive tool to pry up the hive cover and to loosen frames stuck tight with propolis. And you will need a smoker for driving the bees out of the hive when you wish to gather the honeycombs. The smoker is a metal cylinder the size of a coffeepot. It has a spout at the tip and a bellows fastened to the side. The cylinder is stuffed with slow-burning burlap or wood

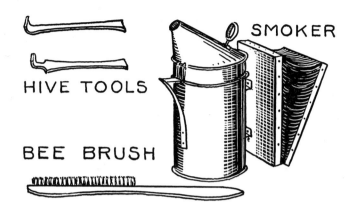

SMOKER

HIVE TOOLS

BEE BRUSH

shavings, lighted and kept burning by air from the bellows. The smoke comes out the spout and is puffed over the combs. It must be cool so as not to burn the bees.

A good beekeeper uses little smoke. His movements are slow and rhythmical to keep the bees from becoming excited. Beginners often wear special gloves with long cuffs to prevent bees from crawling up their sleeves.

Beekeepers try to wear light-colored, smooth clothing, for bees seem to dislike dark cloth and fuzzy material. A pair of bicycle clips around the bottom of your jeans will keep bees from crawling up your legs. Bright colored socks may mean several stings around your ankles. Most satisfactory for wear in the apiary are high boots into which you can tuck your trouser legs. When you are so dressed, no bee can get at you and you need have no fear.

Concerning equipment for housing the bees and managing them, your county agent or any beeman can advise you. Or you can write to a bee supply house and get the information. You will need to give each colony two hive bodies for brood rearing and the storing of honey and pollen. Each colony will also require from four to six supers to hold the extra honey you expect to remove.

You may not get to know all of the 1800 or more kinds of plants, shrubs, and trees of our country that contain food sought by bees, but you will want to know about those in your neighborhood.

Since a swamp is a never-failing source of nectar and pollen, you will be fortunate if you have one near your apiary. If you live in the tropics your bees may have no trouble finding food every day in the year. But if you live far enough north to have distinct changes of season, it is interesting to watch the searching bees move from one source of supply to another.

Early in the spring, bees hover over the yellow catkins of willow trees, eager for the pollen the catkins are ready to shed. Maybe they have used up their winter supply, or perhaps they'd like fresh bread for a change. They fly out when it is still so cold that by the time they reach the alighting board with full baskets they are stiff with the chill. Beekeepers sometimes take pity on these hardy souls and warm them indoors before returning them to the hive.

The tiny early spring flowers of the woods— bloodroot, spring beauties, anemones, bluets, lovely as they are to look at—have no attraction for bees. Even the arbutus with its heavy fragrance contains no nectar. But trees are blooming at this time, and there the bees gather eagerly. This fresh food must taste good to a colony that has been getting along on last fall's aster honey or perhaps eating the flavorless sugar sirup supplied by the beekeeper.

The beekeeper does all he can to obtain strong colonies. He sees to it that the bees have a good laying queen, plenty of space, and no disease. He prevents swarming if he can.

Blossoms of apple, cherry, peach, pear, and other fruit and nut trees all help to feed the steadily mounting number of bee babies, as the queen speeds up her laying. The locust trees droop their white fragrant flowers and the bees are sure to find any that may be in the neighborhood.

The pace of the season's activities now heightens, reaching its peak in June and July. Dandelions and many other wild flowers, clover, alfalfa, basswood or linden trees, tupelo trees, and some gums follow each other in rapid succession, or several of these plants bloom at the same time. The bees work frantically trying to fill every cell in the hive. This is the time for the beekeeper to take his share. He removes a full super and puts back an empty one again and again, and his partners do not fail him. They work for him every sunny day until they are frazzled and old, and finally die with their boots on.

Next come the dog days of August. Hot, dry weather sets in, the flow of nectar slackens, the sun goes down earlier each evening. Now the summer flowers wither and their places are taken by goldenrod, aster, and buckwheat. These plants give the bees nectar and pollen to keep the colony going until the next spring. If the gatherers are not able to find enough, the bee-keeper adds to their supplies. Then with nothing more to gather, the bees and beekeeper take a well-earned rest from the field.

Even if you never become a beekeeper, you may enjoy a hive or two in your backyard for the fun of watching bees at work and for the honey you may provide for the family.

In glimpsing the life within the hive from this book, I hope you have gathered some idea of the infinite variety of ways in which living creatures manage to exist. Each one is unique in its way of life, but none has a more fascinating, more complex life history than does the honeybee.

Books About Beekeeping

The Hive and the Honeybee by Roy A. Grout and others. Dadant & Sons, Inc., Hamilton, Illinois.

Fundamentals of Bee Culture. Bulletin 418A. Colorado Agricultural and Mechanical College, Fort Collins, Colorado.

Beekeeping for Profit and Pleasure by Addison Webb. The Macmillan Company, New York.

Starting Right with Bees. A. I. Root Company, Medina, Ohio.

Bees' Ways by George DeClyver Curtis. Houghton Mifflin Company, Boston.

First Lesson in Beekeeping by C. P. Dadant. Hamilton, Illinois.

ABC and XYZ of Beekeeping by A. I. Root and others. Medina, Ohio.

Beekeeping by E. F. Phillips. The Macmillan Company, New York.

The World of the Honeybee by Colin G. Butler. The Macmillan Company, New York.

Bee Journals

American Bee Journal. Dadant & Sons, Inc., Hamilton, Illinois.
Gleanings in Bee Culture. A. I. Root Company, Medina, Ohio.
Modern Beekeeping. Walter T. Kelley Company, Clarkson, Kentucky.

Bee Supply Houses

Dadant & Sons, Inc., Hamilton, Illinois
Walter T. Kelley Company, Clarkson, Kentucky
A. I. Root Company, Medina, Ohio
Superior Honey Company, Los Angeles, California

Index

About the Author

Mary Geisler Phillips was first introduced to bees when she met Everett Franklin Phillips. He later became her husband, and a world authority on the honeybee and beekeeping. After their marriage the honeybee was as much a part of the family as the children. There were always beehives nearby and honey jars on the table every meal.

Whenever the family traveled it was always a "bee trip," says Mrs. Phillips. The one objective was to meet beemen, a fascinating pursuit that often took them to out-of-the-way places. In 1932, for example, they spent three months in Russia observing bees at the invitation of the Soviet government. They spent many months, too, with Karl von Frisch in Vienna, talking about bees and studying them.

Mrs. Phillips, a native Philadelphian, was graduated from the University of Pennsylvania with a degree in biology. She has been a high school teacher, an editor, a radio script writer, an associate professor, and is now a professor emeritus of Cornell University. She has three sons and five grandchildren.

About the Artist

Elizabeth Burckmyer is a close friend of Mrs. Phillips. She was born in California and came to Cornell University to obtain a master's degree in biology. While at Cornell she married, and she has been there ever since. During the time her two boys were growing up she did free-lance illustrating. Then she took a teaching job and is now associate professor of free-hand drawing at Cornell.